REST AT ITS BEST

C·R·E·A·T·I·O·N Health

LIFE GUIDE #2

For Individual Study and Small Group Use

CREATION Health Life Guide #2

Published by Florida Hospital Publishing
900 Winderley Place, Suite 1600
Maitland, Florida 32751

To Extend *the* Health *and* Healing Ministry *of* Christ

Publisher and Editor-in-Chief: Todd Chobotar
Managing Editor: David Biebel, DMin
Production: Lillian Boyd
Promotion: Laurel Prizigley
Copy Editor: Mollie Braga
Photographer: Timothy Brown
Design: Carter Design, Inc.
Peer Reviewers: Amaryllis Sanchez-Wohlever, MD; Robert Hayes
Rev. Robert Schmalzle, MDiv, MSW; Eli Kim, MD
Barbara Olsen, MACL; Sabine Vatel, DMin
Andy McDonald, DMin; Tim Goff, MDiv
Rick Szilagyi, DMin; Gerald Wasmer, MDiv
Andre VanHeerden; Paul Campoli, MDiv

For volume discounts please contact special sales at:
HealthProducts@FLHosp.org | 407-303-1929

Printed in the United States of America.
PR 14 13 12 11 10 9 8 7 6 5 4 3 2 1
ISBN: 978-0-9839881-6-8

For more life-changing resources visit:
FloridaHospitalPublishing.com
Healthy100Churches.org
CREATIONHealth.com
Healthy100.org

CONTENTS

WELCOME TO CREATION HEALTH

Congratulations on your choice to use this resource to improve your life! Whether you are new to the concept of CREATION Health or are a seasoned expert, this book was created for you. CREATION Health is a faith-based health and wellness program based on the Bible's Creation story. This book is part of a Life Guide series seeking to help you apply eight elegantly simple principles for living life to the full.

The letters of the CREATION acronym stand for:

In John 10:10 Jesus said, "I have come that they may have life, and have it to the full" (NIV). The Greek word used for life is "zoe," which means the absolute fullness of life...genuine life...a life that is active, satisfying, and filled with joy.

That is why CREATION Health takes a life-transforming approach to total person wellness – mentally, physically, spiritually, and socially – with the eight universal principles of health. Where did these principles come from?

The book of Genesis describes how God created the earth and made a special garden called Eden as a home for his first two children, Adam and Eve. One of the first and finest gifts given to them was abundant health. By examining the Creation story we can learn much about feeling fit and living long, fulfilling lives today.

As you begin this journey toward an improved lifestyle, remember that full health is more than the absence of disease and its symptoms. It's a realization that God desires each of his children – people like you and me whom he loves and cares about – to have the best that this life can offer. It is trusting that your Creator has a plan for your life.

Is there any good parent who doesn't want the best for their child? No. So it makes sense that God would want his best for us. Naturally, human freedom of choice sometimes makes life messy, so not everything can or will be perfect as it once was. But that doesn't mean we shouldn't take a good look at the earliest records of humans found in the Bible to see if there is something special that can be gleaned.

This book – and the other seven in the Life Guide series – takes a deep dive into CREATION Health and translates the fundamental concepts into easy-to-follow steps. These guides include many questions designed to help you or your small group plumb the depths of every principle and learn strategies for integrating the things you learn into everyday life. As a result, you will discover that embracing the CREATION Health prescription can help restore health, happiness, balance, and joy to life.

The CREATION Health Lifestyle has a long, proven history of wellness and longevity – worldwide! People just like you are making a few simple changes in their lives and living longer, fuller lives. They are getting healthy, staying healthy, and are able to do the things they love, well into their later years. Now is the time to join them by transforming your habits into a healthy lifestyle.

If you would like to learn more about the many resources available, visit **CREATIONHealth.com**. If you would like to learn more about how to live to a Healthy 100, visit **Healthy100.org** or visit **Healthy100Churches.org**.

Welcome to CREATION Health,

Todd Chobotar
Publisher and Editor-in-Chief

VALUING SLEEP

LESSON ONE

WARM UP

Choose one or both questions to discuss (if in group setting) or write out your answers on a separate sheet (for individual use):

1. **Describe your first paid job. What did you do with the money?**[1]

2. **Where would you like to go for one day anywhere in the world? Why?**[2]

"Sometimes the most urgent thing you can possibly do is take a complete rest."

ASHLEIGH BRILLIANT

DISCOVERY

My car should be an embarrassment. The maroon colored paint has large blotches and fade marks due to sun exposure. The felt material across the ceiling has become unglued in places, causing it to sag like an old man's jowls. Two out of the four inside door handles are completely dysfunctional. To get out of the driver's seat, I have to open the window, open the door from the outside, raise the window, and then exit. I'm sure the car needs some kind of maintenance that I'm too lazy to read about or track. When I have to take a friend somewhere, I usually say, "I'm driving my *old* car." That intentional inflection is sort of a lie. It leaves the door open for the friend to assume that I have another car that is showroom slick. I don't. The problem is that I don't really care all that much about my non-slick vehicle.

Unlike my car, however, I am *very* concerned about the maintenance record for my brain and the rest of my body. They have quite a few miles on them at this point and the stakes are much higher than for my auto.

For some time, we have been exposed to a huge emphasis on the importance of proper nutrition and exercise. These two biggies are all over the airways and bookshelves. Veggies, fruits, nuts, and grains get gobs of press, along with the need to walk, jump, stretch, and bend. Rightly so. Proper nutrition and exercise are certainly crucial to optimal brain functioning and overall health.

The problem is that we hear very little about another topic that is *extremely important – sleep,* though it is as vital as air and water.[3] The only time sleep is mentioned in the media is in a TV ad where some lovely person yawns gracefully and a smooth-voiced pitch man invites us to purchase pastel colored pills while soothing music bathes the moment in a soft, beguiling melody.

We spend roughly one third of our lives sleeping and yet the average person pays more attention to their car or pet than to their slumber. People may have a vague notion that we ought to get enough sleep, but it is far from a burning issue. For the average person it remains in the backwater of conversations regarding their personal well-being.

We don't *value* sleep because we don't *understand* the intricate processes that occur during those hours of shut-eye. Bedtime appears to be simply "down time." It appears to be a biological mini-vacation; a wasteland of missed opportunities to get more done at work or at home; a temporary detour from our goals and dreams. We lop time off from either end of sleep in order to devote time to "more important things." That's why we don't feel guilty sleeping as little as possible.

The truth can provide a much needed wake-up-call. Far from being "down-time," sleep allows a carefully orchestrated set of essential biological activities that we ignore at our peril. What occurs during those nocturnal hours is a complex, dynamic set of processes, truly wondrous to behold.

Picture the following. It's 10:30 p.m. and you're staring at the TV between increasingly frequent, face-contorting yawns. It's time to hit the power switch on the remote. You then turn off the living room light, turn down the heat, drag yourself to the master bathroom, brush your teeth, put on your jammies, click off the lamp on the nightstand, and slip under the linen covers. If you are a well-rested person, you'll take about ten to fifteen minutes to enter into Stage 1 of your multi-faceted sleep journey. Falling asleep immediately is usually a sign of sleep deprivation.[4]

We don't value sleep because we don't understand the intricate processes that occur during those hours of shut-eye.

There are five stages of sleep. Stage 1 occurs only once, at the beginning, and is transitional. It takes you from wakefulness to unconsciousness. You become unaware of the clock ticking, the dog barking across the street, the slight hum of the overhead fan, the motor noise from the refrigerator cooling system. Your body temperature begins to drop, muscles relax, and your eyes move slowly from side to side under your eyelids.[5] You twitch occasionally, just enough to annoy your spouse.

The sequence of sleep stages for the brain is automatic and fixed: 2, 3, 4, 2, REM (Rapid Eye Movement). That pattern, or cycle, repeats itself throughout the night until we awaken. Each cycle takes about ninety to one hundred minutes.[6] While you snore, a neural symphony is happening inside your head. Your brain is often, in fact, more active during sleep than when you are awake.[7] During the entire night, we spend more than half of our sleep time in stage 2, approximately 20 percent in REM, and the rest of the time in stages 3 and 4.[8] *How well these sleep stages are able to fulfill their functions has a direct influence on the quality of all our daytime hours.*

About five minutes after falling asleep, you slip into stage 2, a deeper level of unconsciousness. What happens during this stage makes you feel more attentive and alert during the day. It keeps your nose from falling into the binding of your notebook during a late morning meeting at work. It prevents you from dosing off at the wheel or having your mind drift while your spouse carefully recounts his/her day.[9]

During stage 2 the thalamus, which is instrumental in passing along messages from our senses, takes its own siesta. By largely shutting down, it gives the brain a rest from the thousands and thousands of signals it normally receives. Other parts of the brain put their feet up on the sofa and relax, as well, areas involved with language, reasoning, planning, problem solving, and social interactions, among others.[10]

If you are trying to learn how to drive a car, operate machinery, play golf, tennis, or master other types of sequential motor movements, then stage 2 is for you. Without the magical welding of circuitry that occurs during this phase, we'd be a whole lot more awkward than some of us already are. I'd still be using the "Columbus Method" of typing on a keyboard – discover and land. During slumber, crucial neural pathways are deepened and defined.[11]

Outside your home a police siren wails, a jet roars overhead, someone's car alarm goes off, a teenager lays down some tire rubber, but you are completely oblivious. About twenty to thirty minutes have gone by since lights out and your brain has now ventured into stages 3 and 4, a period of what is called "Slow Wave Sleep," or SWS. Stage 3 has both theta and delta waves, whereas stage 4 has only delta.[12]

Body temperature lowers. Muscles relax further. Breathing becomes shallower. The firing of neural connections slows dramatically. Blood supply to the brain is minimal. Stage 4 sleep is the deepest. It's like going from a dimly lit tunnel into a dark cave. Cranially speaking, you've definitely gone subterranean. Wake up from here and you'll feel mentally groggy for a few minutes.[13]

During stages 3 and 4, many events occur that are crucial to your well-being. Your tissues and organs get a break from the urgent, arduous, wearying daytime prod of the "stress hormone" cortisol.[14] At the same time, the pea-sized pituitary gland at the base of your brain steps up to the plate and delivers a powerful jolt of growth hormone throughout your system to restore your tissues and organs to peak performance and stimulate growth and development.[15] We might compare the work of growth hormone to the horde of theme park employees who come out during the night to build, fix, paint, and clean before sunrise. If you essentially cut back the employees' hours by cutting back on your sleep, your body will eventually suffer from disrepair.

Many of the fats and carbohydrates you loaded up on at the convenience store and fast food restaurant get processed now and are given the bum's rush out of your body. Short change this process and the goop eagerly takes up residence on your belly and thighs.[16]

The brain also clears out old, unused neural pathways to make way for new learning. It prunes the deadwood on the tree of knowledge, uncluttering your mind and creating space for your next brilliant ideas and insights.[17] Why should your brain have to remember the phone number you had twenty moves ago or the name of the person you desperately wanted to date in high school?

After briefly cycling back to stage 2, your brain enthusiastically enters the most exciting period of all – REM sleep. Your brain goes from strolling in the woods at the state park to racing down the highway, passing trucks and wide-eyed grannies.

The bed sheets and blankets stir and shift as you take in gulps of air to fuel the next portion of your nocturnal journey. Your heart speeds up, blood vessels expand, blood pressure rises, and the temperature of your body decreases while your brain heats up. Neurons fire at their highest level so far. Under closed eyelids, your eyeballs quickly scan back and forth as if frantically searching.[18]

Cue the projector. The movie screen of your mind comes alive. Dreamtime is here. Once again you are shoved on stage without having memorized your lines. You nervously sit down for a big final exam you somehow thought was next week. You also get attacked by a huge, two-headed animal in the wilds of Borneo. By the way, because you might be tempted to run from the animal and wake up on the bedroom floor with a hurt back, your brain has conveniently paralyzed you from head to toe during REM sleep. It goes away later. Didn't I tell you this was exciting![19]

This is when a lot of new information is organized and filed in your memory banks.[20] It's as if a large team of file clerks is scurrying around between your ears carefully categorizing and storing papers and Post-it notes that have accumulated during the day. They also relate them properly to similar existing files and folders. Cutting back on sleep cuts back significantly on what you're able to retain because you imprudently chose to lock out the file clerks. If you want to recall facts later, sleep on them well. Otherwise they could vaporize tomorrow like the morning dew.[21]

We are always in danger of losing key information we need to retain if pathways in the brain are seldom accessed. "Use it or lose it" is the general rule. REM sleep has that covered in an amazing way. It is able to discern which old pathways should be preserved and randomly fires up a portion of them each night to keep them stimulated, healthy, and available.[22]

REM sleep is also where much of our creativity originates. That innovative answer to the complex problem you've been wrestling with seemed to come out of the blue during breakfast. Actually, that was all worked out during the night and the rest of your brain is just now getting the memo.[23]

In relation to sleep in general, research has confirmed that when we don't get enough sleep and the brain is not allowed to perform all of its positive magic, we develop a significantly greater risk for:

1. **Weight gain**
2. **Hardening of the arteries**
3. **High blood pressure**
4. **Heart attack and stroke**
5. **Diabetes**
6. **Colds and flu**
7. **Colon and breast cancer**
8. **Allergies and asthma**
9. **Emotional upsets and instability.**[24]

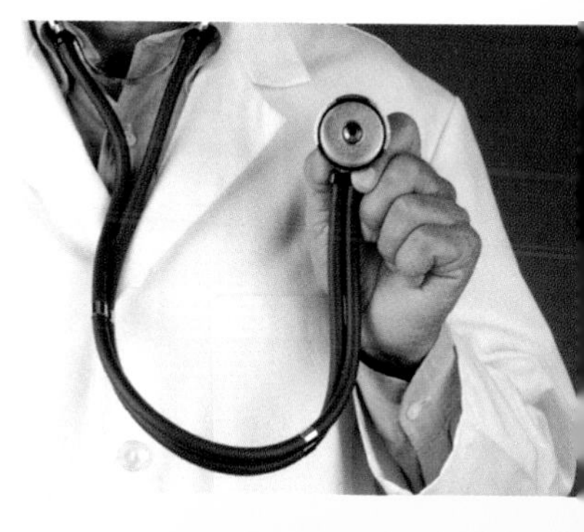

Adequate sleep is power. Full, consistent sleep is vital for optimal living and happiness. It is an incredible gift from the hand of our Creator. I can think of no greater endorsement of the importance of sleep than from the great apostle Paul. His enemies had called into question the apostle's Christian leadership, credentials, and commitment. Paul answered by listing the enormous difficulties he had to overcome in order to spread the gospel: beatings, imprisonment, riots, stoning, shipwrecks, perils from robbers, etc. Right in the middle of that horrendous, debilitating list, the apostle included a hardship that many might consider out of place – *sleeplessness*. But for Paul, sufficient sleep was something he highly valued and missed greatly when he couldn't get it (see 2 Cor. 6:3-7; 2 Cor. 11:25-28).

DISCUSSION

Have you ever continued to use something that was worn out like I did with my car?

How are you most affected by a lack of sleep?

Are you able to remember any of your dreams after you wake up? Can you recall a recent one?

Name one important event/process that is going on in your brain during each of the following phases of sleep:

STAGE 2

STAGE 3

STAGE 4

REM

What most surprised you about what goes on during sleep?

What sleep benefit is the most relevant for you right now?

How has your attitude toward sleep changed after reading this lesson?

In what way do you think lack of sleep might have affected the apostle Paul the most?

SHARING

OPPORTUNITY #1

This section is about an opportunity for you to be a blessing to someone outside of your small group and to also deepen the impact of the lesson on your own life. The group is encouraged to discuss at the end of each meeting what aspects of the lesson they might like to share with someone at home, work, or in the community if the opportunity arises. *There is "An Abundant Living Thought" at the end of each lesson as one possibility of something to pass along.*

Start each day asking God to provide opportunities to share and then keep your radar up.

You can be an ambassador and reach people with the good news that abundant living is available to all.

ABUNDANT LIVING THOUGHT

Far from being "down-time," sleep is a carefully orchestrated set of essential biological activities that we ignore at our peril. What occurs during those nocturnal hours is a complex, dynamic set of processes, truly wondrous to behold.

SLEEPING WELL

LESSON TWO

WARM UP

Feedback: In what ways did God open the door last week for you share some part of the lessons with someone else?

Choose one or both questions to discuss (if in group setting) or write out your answers on a separate sheet (for individual use):

1. **If you could, what kind of charitable organization would you like to establish?**[25]

2. **In one sentence, what advice should parents give their children when they get married?**

> *"Finish each day before you begin the next, and interpose a solid wall of sleep between the two."*
>
> **RALPH WALDO EMERSON**

DISCOVERY

I never liked my silver saxophone very much. As far as I knew, everyone else in the saxophone universe had one that was colored a gleaming, stately gold. Silver saxophones were the hue of musical odd balls. It was, however, all my low income parents could afford to rent from the local music store during my fifth year in grade school.

It not only looked strange, it also played reluctantly, very reluctantly. You had to blow your brains out to hit a wobbly high C musical note. Despite regular formal lessons, squeaks, squawks, and periodic yelps were the embarrassing norm.

On Thanksgiving Day, our family visited my cousins who lived at least five or six rungs further up the social ladder from us. Bored waiting for dinner, I wandered into my cousin Doug's bedroom and spotted what looked like a saxophone case sticking out from under his bed. I pulled the pristine case out carefully, opened the cover, and was astonished to find the gleaming, gold-colored sax I had dreamed about so often.

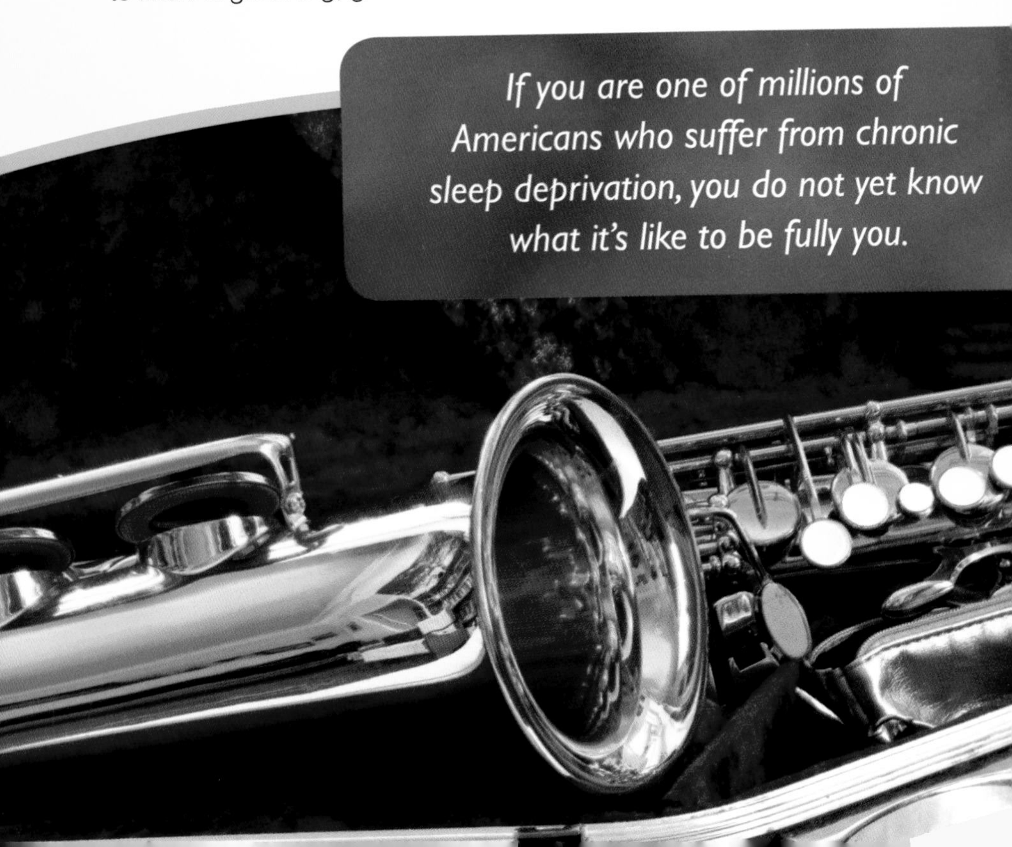

At that very moment Doug entered the room. "Do you play saxophone?" he asked.

"Yah," I replied, "but mine's a real antique."

"Want to borrow that one? I don't play anymore," he offered.

I jumped at the chance. At home, I couldn't believe how easy it was to hit musical notes now! It was the difference between running with slippers and running with brand new, NBA-approved sneakers. It was almost effortless. I felt transported. No more noises that weren't on the sheet music. It was exhilarating.

Think for a minute of your body and brain as being like a saxophone. If you're not getting enough sleep, you probably feel like I did playing my silver horn. It produces, but too often with considerable reluctance and difficulty. In this lesson, we'll talk about how to transform that old silver sax into a gold one. We'll discuss how to get enough sleep so you can take your life to a whole new level.

If you are one of millions of Americans who suffer from chronic sleep deprivation, you do not yet know what it's like to be fully you. There is a good chance that there is a gleaming version of yourself that you've rarely, if ever, experienced. Dr. James B. Maas puts it well, "We slowly habituate ourselves over time to a low level of alertness thinking that how we feel now is normal. The truth is that most of us are functioning at a level far from optimal, far from the level of alertness that enables us to be energetic, wide awake, happy, creative, productive, motivated, and healthy human beings."[26]

Instead, people drag themselves through each day with eighty percent of Americans now relying on coffee or some other pick-me-up to get them through.[27]

Before the invention of the light bulb, people used to average between nine and ten hours of sleep per night. Researchers have demonstrated that even people who now regularly get eight hours of sleep function at a significantly higher level when that is extended.[28] *Today that nine to ten hour mark has shrunk to an alarming average of 6.7 hours.*[29] Generally speaking, our nation is tired and at risk from lack of sleep.

High school and college students are without doubt some the most sleep-deprived groups in our society. Drowsiness is common and surveys indicate that up to thirty percent of students fall asleep in class at least one time per week.[30]

In the last twenty years people have, on average, added 158 hours annually to their working and commuting time. Women with young children have added 241 such hours since 1969. All typically at the cost of adequate sleep.[31] A 2005 study discovered that almost three in ten workers either missed work or made work errors due to sleep related issues they experienced over a three month period.[32] Fifty-one percent of workers indicate that sleepiness interferes with the amount of work they can do.[33]

The National Highway Traffic Safety Administration conservatively estimates that sleepy drivers cause over 100,000 reported accidents each year with 76,000 injuries and 15,000 deaths.[34] The actual number is probably much higher if you add in non-highway crashes. Lack of sleep can be similar in its effects to alcohol.[35]

One of the most appalling demonstrations of the debilitating effects of sleep deprivation in history can be seen in the Garden of Gethsemane on the night before Jesus' crucifixion. Jerusalem was a hotbed of hate toward the Savior. The air was electric with danger for Christ and the disciples. Troubles had been escalating all week and were rapidly reaching the boiling point. Mobs were being assembled. Weapons handed out.

Thursday evening Jesus retreated to Gethsemane, presumably to gather his thoughts and pray. His only request of the disciples was *please stay awake and pray as well* (see Matt. 26:38, 41). He then knelt down several yards away and pleaded with his Father. Three times he returned to the disciples to make sure they were paying attention at this critical hour. The fate of the whole world hung in the balance, yet each time he returned his closest companions were *fast asleep!* A week of high stress and deep sadness had taken its toll (see Luke 22:45).

Adults do not all need the same amount of sleep, *but a large segment of American society needs to get at least sixty to ninety more minutes of sleep each night.*[36] That also holds true for senior citizens who, contrary to popular myth, do not need less sleep.[37] So how much sleep do *you* need? Enough to make you feel fully rested and alert and enough to give the stages of sleep time to do their vital tasks.

As we discussed in the previous lesson, lack of sleep can stem from underestimating its value and not giving it priority. *It can also be the product of bad sleep habits.* No surprise here. When do parents ever sit their children down and explain *how* to sleep? They probably model just the opposite. What school teaches a class called "Sleep 101?" When is it ever a part of pre-marital counseling? What employer sends his employees to seminars entitled, "Snooze or Lose"?

Thankfully, there are a number of ways you can help yourself get a better night's sleep by incorporating some or all of the following suggestions. Remember, what works for one person may not work for another, so experiment:

1. **Pay attention not only to the quantity of sleep but to the quality as well.** The key is whether you wake up feeling rested and refreshed or not, no matter how many hours you spend in bed.
2. **Stress, depression, and anxiety can interrupt sleep.** Look for ways to resolve these underlying issues.
3. **Exercise can dramatically improve sleep.** Cardiovascular is better than strength training, getting your heart rate up and your muscles moving for at least twenty minutes three or four times a week.[38]

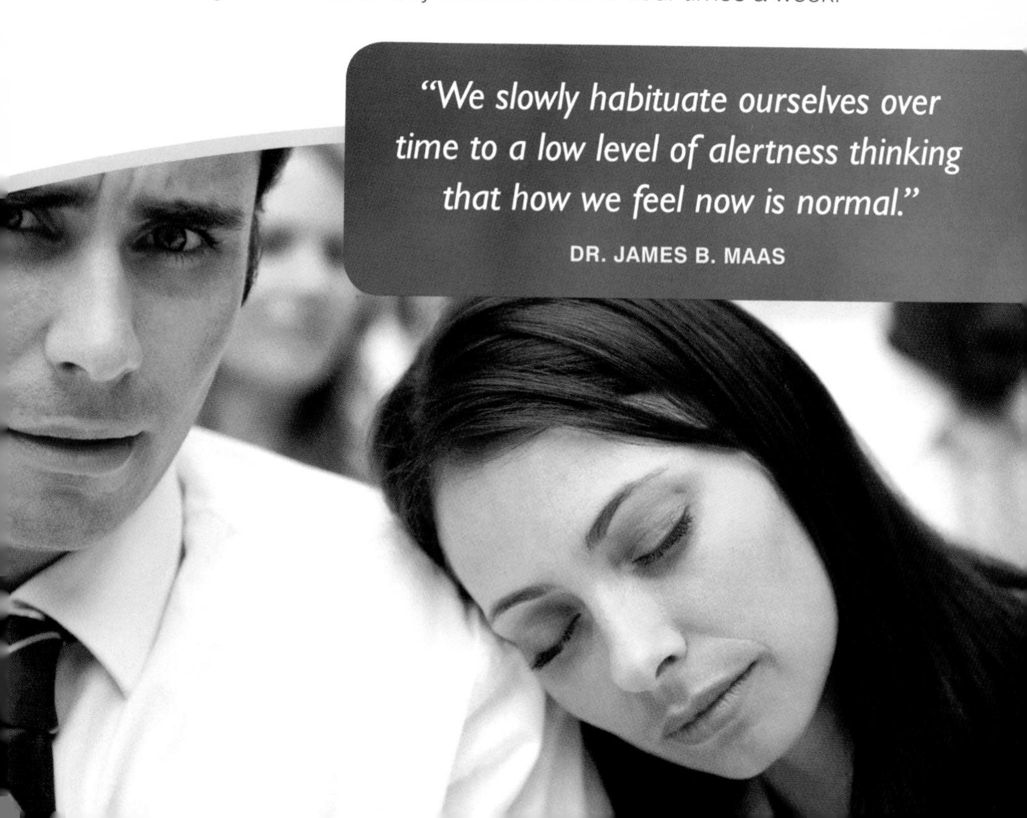

4. **The time when sleep begins is important.** Getting to bed between 9 and 11 p.m. is most in harmony with our body's natural rhythms and melatonin production.[39] To find a bedtime that works for you, take the time you get up in the morning and count back eight hours. For example, if you get up at 6:30 a.m., then you should be in bed by 10:30 p.m. the night before. *Consider that your personal curfew and make it an important priority.* Set your cell phone alarm to alert you at least fifteen to twenty minutes ahead of 10:30 p.m. to allow time to get ready.[40] Slowly adjust that bedtime up or down in fifteen minute increments until you are able to wake up within ten minutes of your morning target without an alarm clock.[41] Be patient with yourself. Changing old habits is a journey.

5. **Don't consume heavy meals within three hours of bedtime.** For some people, however, going to bed with an empty stomach can also be a problem. Go for a snack that combines carbs and a little bit of protein such as peanut butter, crackers and cheese, cottage cheese and bananas, oats, dates, figs, honey, etc.[42] Also avoid caffeine, spices, and high fat foods in the evening. It is best to give up alcohol and smoking altogether.[43]

6. **Keep the bedroom in dim light leading up to sleep and completely dark during sleep itself.** Bright says "daytime" and dim says "time to wind things down." Use a night light to illuminate your way to the bathroom at night instead of turning the lights up. If you do get up during the night, you might even try keeping one eye closed in order to avoid signaling your brain to wake up.[44]

7. **Get some sunshine during the morning to help regulate your biological clock.** No sun all day and bright lights at home in the evening can send the wrong signals to your internal timer. You need melatonin in order to sleep. Light inhibits its release and darkness enhances it.[45]

8. **Get the smart phone, TV, and computer out of the bedroom.** You need to use the bedroom only for sleep and intimacy.

9. **Avoid excessive mental stimulation before crawling under the covers.** If you can't get something off your mind, write it down and leave it until morning.

10. **Start winding down before going to bed.** Utilize calming techniques such as deep breathing, meditation, and/or progressive muscle relaxation before bedtime. When you get to bed, mentally visualize pleasant, restful scenes and experiences from your past.

11. **Develop nighttime rituals and routines** that make a clear separation for your brain between wake time and sleep time. Try a warm bath, soft music, a warm drink, reading before getting into bed, etc.

12. **Don't lie in bed for more than twenty to thirty minutes without sleeping.** Get up, do something relaxing, and try again. You don't want to associate bed with frustration. Six hours of solid sleep is better than eight hours of fragmented sleep.[46]

13. **Don't try too hard to sleep.** Make relaxation, not sleeping, the goal.

14. **Keep the bedroom cool, well ventilated, and quiet.** Use "white noise" machines or earplugs if necessary to shut out noise.

15. **Set a regular time to sleep and wake up.** Stick to it as much as possible, even on weekends. Make up for shortages as soon as possible. If you stay up late, get up the same time anyway to keep your bio-clock on schedule. A mid-day nap can overcome any resulting drowsiness.

16. **Lengthen your sleep** by going to bed earlier in fifteen minute increments and increasing that time over several weeks.
17. **Create a pleasant, restful décor for your bedroom.** Avoid clutter. Making your bed in the morning makes it more inviting at night.
18. **Turn your mattress over** every few months and replace it every five to seven years.[47]
19. **Get a well made pillow** that fits your needs and keeps your body in a straight alignment.
20. **If none of these tips provide the help you need, carefully consider seeing a qualified medical sleep specialist.**

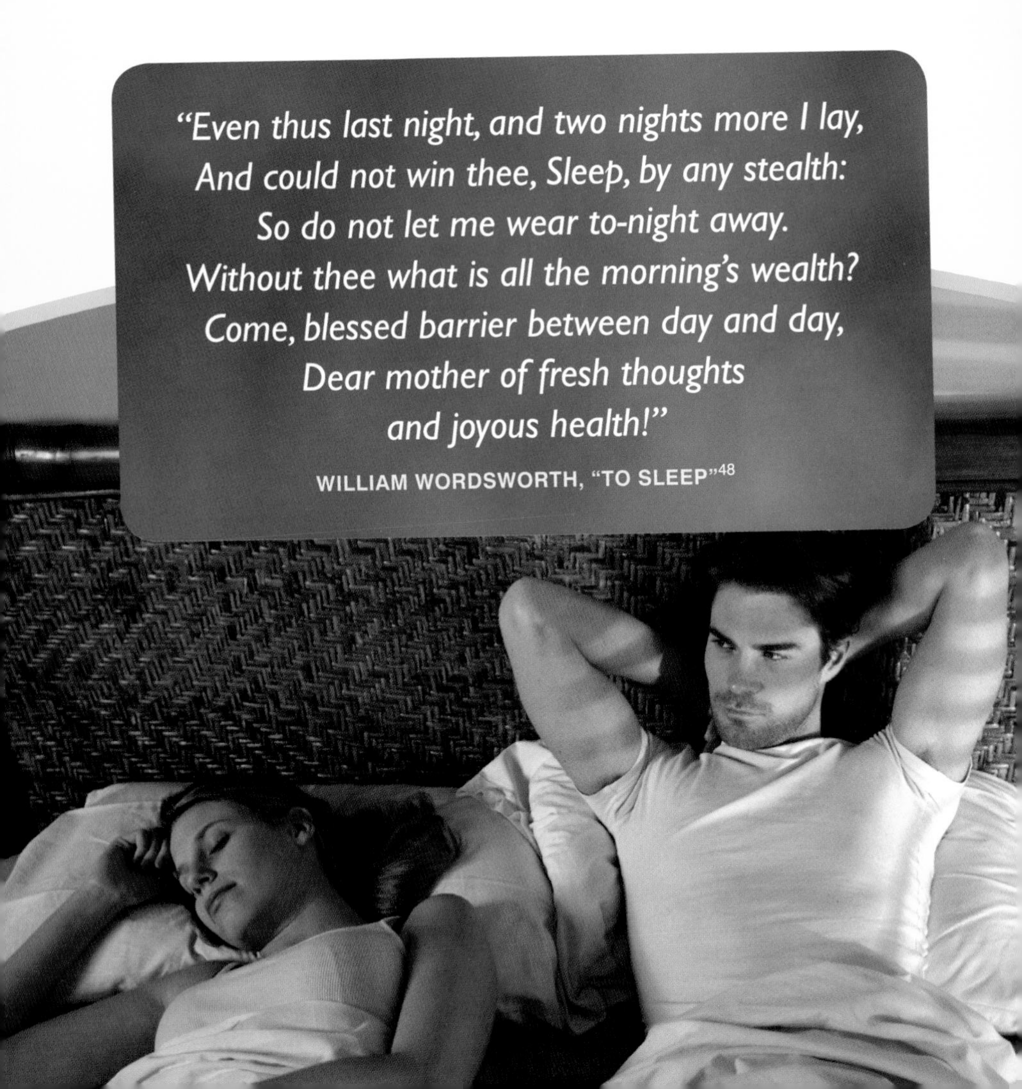

NOTES:

Christ talks about "rest for your souls," rest for your inner self, that sensitive place where anxiety and stress normally hang out and bully you around.

DISCUSSION

What situations make it hard for you to sleep?

How much more sleep do you feel you need?

What are you like when you don't get enough sleep?

Do you feel pressure to sleep less and get more done? How could that pressure be lessened?

Are you more of a night owl or an early bird? Is that beneficial or does it need to change?

Select *two* items on the list of twenty suggestions for better sleep that you feel would be most effective. Explain why you made those selections.

How would your life be enhanced if you could feel truly rested at the beginning of each day?

What specific change can you make this week to sleep better?

SHARING

OPPORTUNITY #2

- Pray for God to open the way for you to share something from these lessons to help someone else this week.
- Keep your radar up each day for opportunities.

ABUNDANT LIVING THOUGHT

Adults do not all need the same amount of sleep, but a large segment of American society needs to get at least sixty to ninety more minutes of sleep each night.

NAP POWER

LESSON THREE

WARM UP

Feedback: In what ways did God open the door last week for you share some part of the lessons with someone else?

....

....

....

....

Choose one or both questions to discuss (if in group setting) or write out your answers on a separate sheet (for individual use):

1. **What possession do you care about the most? Explain.**[49]

....

....

....

2. **Have you ever been lost? Explain.**[50]

....

....

....

"Rest when you're weary. Refresh and renew yourself, your body, your mind, your spirit. Then get back to work."

RALPH MARSTON

DISCOVERY

I propose that we no longer take showers or baths except on weekends. Sure we'll all smell bad and look grimy during the week, but there are too many benefits to maintain the current obsession with daily hygiene.

Shares of soap stock will probably take a dip on the New York Stock Exchange. But people simply need to redirect their investments to shares of perfume, cologne, and air freshener. One caution. There is the old adage, "If we all stink, no one stinks," so be careful not to over-invest. It's similar to what would happen if everyone ate garlic. The odor becomes the new normal and eventually no one notices.

The main advantage of my proposal is to have more time to rush around and get more done, both at work and at home. Fifteen to twenty extra minutes a day adds up and you can always get clean on the weekends. After all, productivity is the name of the game in the Western World. Busyness is king. Who hasn't said to themselves, "If I only had more time to do this or that!" Corporations are squeezing employees to accomplish more. Overtime is growing. Take-home work is expanding. In the face of those pressing realities, eliminating weekday showers is the best answer I can come up with at the moment.

Of course my proposal is tongue in cheek, a meager attempt at satire. I can't imagine society forgoing showers for the sake of productivity. People wouldn't let societal pressures keep them from engaging in such a valuable personal routine. But, remarkably, that is exactly what has happened to what used to be another valuable personal routine – *napping*. Napping in the afternoon was a daily practice for much of the world for many centuries. Historian A. Roger Ekirch says, "Napping is a tool as old as time itself."[51] For most of human history, rest during the day was thought to be as important as sleeping at night.

Much of that has now changed, however. For large numbers of people, it has simply dropped off the radar. The idea of getting some shut-eye in the afternoon doesn't even occur to them. They forego naps all week and then nap on the weekends to try and catch up.

How could such a dramatic change occur? Some background can help. In the first century BC, the Romans sectioned their day into time for designated activities such as prayer, meals, and rest. The sixth hour, noon, came to be known as *sexta*, when everyone would go to bed. The word has survived as the modern day *siesta*.[52] There was a time when much of Europe saw the afternoon nap, or siesta, as sacrosanct. For two hours each day businesses stopped, shutters closed, and the vast majority of people snoozed.

The invention of mechanical timepieces during the 13th and 14th centuries ushered in a shift in attitudes. Time could now be divided up into hours, minutes, and seconds. Instead of being paid by the job, workers got paid by the hour. The mantra, "Time is money," took root and employers saw sleep during the day as wasteful. The Industrial Revolution solidified that perspective, which continues to this day.[53]

The practice of napping has been reduced to the province of an undervalued minority. It has fallen victim to the pressures and norms of a society that values wealth over well-being and productivity over optimal living. Adults who take afternoon naps too often fear being labeled as lazy, unproductive slackers. Nappers can feel like they have to slink, sneak, and cover up. Modern living has gotten us to compromise. And it is a capitulation with much greater health and lifestyle implications than giving up regular trips to the shower stall.

There was a time when much of Europe saw the afternoon nap, or siesta, as sacrosanct. For two hours each day businesses stopped, shutters closed, and the vast majority of people snoozed.

Based on historical precedent and recent scientific research, napping needs to be restored to its rightful place within the larger subject of rest. The word *nap* needs to be rehabilitated in people's minds so that it can be highly valued once again. Dr. James B. Maas from Cornell University states, "Napping should not be frowned upon at the office or make you feel guilty at home. *It should have the status of daily exercise"* (emphasis added).[54]

Scientists have discovered that we are built to nap. It's right there in the owners' manual. When our core temperature goes down at night we sleep. When it goes up in the morning we feel more alert. When it flattens out, like it does in the early afternoon, we naturally feel sleepy again.[55]

Napping also puts us in harmony with what is called the body's "circadian rhythm," which regulates our periods of wakefulness and sleep. It creates the desire to sleep in two phases, the strongest occurs during the night and the second, also strong, occurs during the afternoon.[56]

Researchers understand that we don't get sleepy after lunch because we ate too much pizza. Human beings were designed by their Creator to be "biphasic."[57] That means that we are supposed to have *two* separate periods of sleep every twenty-four hours, one at night and one in the afternoon.

Unfortunately, many people try to force their bodies and brains to become "monophasic," with only one big chunk of sleep at night. They ignore the natural afternoon sleep period completely. The need for afternoon rest doesn't simply go away, it's still there urging us to comply. We usually push through by ingesting various unhealthy pick-me-ups or we slip unboosted into a mental and physical La La Land of low productivity. And society calls that normal. It doesn't have to be that way.

There are numerous benefits that napping provides, *even for those who are getting a full night's sleep:*

- Matthew Walker, assistant psychology professor at UC Berkeley, has discovered that naps clear space in short-term memory so that the brain can absorb new information. He compares it to an e-mail box that is full until you get some sleep and make way for more.[58]
- Studies of shift workers reveal that a twenty minute nap can enhance alertness, psychomotor performance, and mood.[59]
- Twenty minute power naps lead to impressive increases in productivity among employees.[60] Instead of saying, "I'm too busy to nap," tell yourself, "I'm so busy, I need to nap."
- According to a study published in the *Archives of Internal Medicine* in 2007, people who napped thirty minutes daily were 37 percent less likely to die of heart disease. Naps also significantly bolster the immune system.[61]
- Naps stimulate creativity and problem-solving ability.[62]
- Naps reduce the number of accidents and mistakes.[63]
- Afternoon naps result in more patience, less stress, greater efficiency, increased ability to concentrate, and much better overall health.[64]
- Napping allows you to feel refreshed for the evening with family and friends.

Thankfully there are still a sizable number of people who have built a midday nap into their daily routine, despite society's pressures to the contrary. As awareness of the benefits grows, so does the number of adherents.

Some of the most famous nappers in history include Da Vinci, Napoleon, Thomas Edison, Albert Einstein, John F. Kennedy, Ronald Reagan, George W. Bush, Jim Lehrer from PBS, and Winston Churchill, especially during the horrendous pressures of World War II.[65] Churchill famously said, "Don't think you will be doing less work because you sleep during the day. You will be able to accomplish more."[66]

The great majority of National Basketball Association players are dedicated nappers because of its restorative effects. Adam Silver, the league's deputy commissioner says, "Everyone in the league office knows not to call players at 3 p.m. It's the player nap."[67]

Napping is also catching on with business. They are paying more attention after reports like the one in the Journal of Occupational and Environmental Medicine revealed that fatigued workers cost companies over $136 billion each year in health-related 'LPT,' or lost productive time. In another alarming survey, 51 percent of the American workforce reported that sleepiness at work hinders the volume of work they can get done.[68] Companies like British Airways, Nike, Pizza Hut, and Google have gone so far as to offer nappers reclining chairs and "renewal rooms" for rest.[69]

In his article, "Nap Your Way to the Top," Carlin Flora states, "The evidence is overwhelming: Napping on the job is great for you and great for your boss."[70] It improves the bottom line by boosting employee effectiveness and well-being. In a 2010 article in the *Harvard Business Review*, Tony Schwartz offers the following advice to business leaders, "Napping won't begin to take hold in companies until leaders recognize that it's not the number of hours people work that determines the value they create, but rather the energy they're capable of bringing to whatever hours they work... The problem is that most corporate cultures remain addicted to the draining ethic of more, bigger, faster."[71]

Once we learn to value naps, we then need to pay attention to *how*. There are several key points to keep in mind:

1. **Give yourself permission to nap** and don't feel guilty about it. You need to erase any lingering stigma that your mind may attach to the word *nap*. You are being wise and health conscious. You are following in the footsteps of generations before you. You are doing what your body is designed to do.

2. **The best length for an afternoon nap is fifteen to thirty minutes.** That enables you to complete a full cycle of stage 2 sleep. It is when we wake up in the middle of a sleep stage that we feel groggy. Naps longer than thirty minutes will take you into stages 3 and 4 and make it more likely that these stages will not be finished by the time you awaken.[72]

3. **A fifteen to thirty minute nap anytime between 1-3 p.m.** will not adversely affect your nightly sleep.[73]

4. **Even a nap as short as six minutes** can improve memory and problem-solving.[74]

5. **If you cannot fall asleep,** there is still significant benefit in simply meditating, relaxing any tense muscles, or closing your eyes and reflecting mentally on calming scenes.

6. **When napping at your workplace, keep the following in mind:**[75]

    a. Unless your company has a policy that allows napping during work hours, you should plan to nap during lunch or an afternoon break.

    b. Use your office or some other available space. You may also want to go off premises, perhaps in your car.

    c. Shut out light with an eye mask. Shut out noise by asking someone to hold your calls and turning off your phone.

    d. Use a comfortable chair or place a mat on the floor. Bring a pillow or fold up a towel.

    e. Use a timer to make sure you wake up on time.

    f. After the nap take in several deep breaths, walk around, or splash water on your face.

    g. Start with a shorter nap such as ten to fifteen minutes.

We'll conclude this lesson with a call to action from Bill and Camille Anthony who write, "It's time for nappers to lie down and be counted!"[76]

DISCUSSION

If you are a regular napper, describe your routine. How does it benefit you?

What does the lesson mean when it says that we were "built to nap"?

Describe how you might nap at work without creating a problem.

Would taking a nap make you feel guilty or lazy? Where does that feeling come from?

In the lesson, which *two items* on the list of benefits from napping are most meaningful for you?

If you do not take regular naps, what have you learned from this lesson that might motivate you to start?

Have you ever visited a country or culture where napping is routine? What did you notice?

How could mothers with little children get a nap?

SHARING

OPPORTUNITY #3:

- Pray for God to open the way for you to share something from these lessons to help someone else this week.
- Keep your radar up each day for opportunities.

ABUNDANT LIVING THOUGHT

Give yourself permission to nap and don't feel guilty about it. You need to erase any lingering stigma that your mind may attach to the word nap.

GIVE YOURSELF THE PRESENT

LESSON FOUR

WARM UP

Feedback: In what ways did God open the door last week for you share some part of the lessons with someone else?

Choose one or both questions to discuss (if in group setting) or write out your answers on a separate sheet (for individual use):

1. **What especially caught your interest as a child?**[77]

2. **What is one of the craziest or funniest experiences you've ever had on a trip or vacation?**[78]

"For fast-acting relief, try slowing down."

LILY TOMLIN

DISCOVERY

I had been looking forward all week to watching my favorite sports team on TV in the first round of the playoffs. Game time was set for 8 p.m. The morning of the game, my wife reminded me that the next concert in the series we had paid significant dollars for was that very evening at, you guessed it, 8 p.m. As the orchestra played Brahms, my mind was back on the game, wondering about the score, recounting the match-ups, regretting the scheduling conflict. Then it hit me, *"Hey, dummy. You're missing a great concert with your wife!"* Jolted to my senses, I settled in and had a very uplifting and enjoyable evening. (I later learned that the game was a relatively boring blowout anyway.)

That incident reminded me that being fully present, living in the moment, is a major key to inner rest and calmness. Focusing on the present is foundational to living deliciously, contentedly, and with true serenity.

Life is simply a series of moments, each one as fleeting as a snowflake that lands on your nose then quickly melts away. Just like we are fooled into thinking that a movie is continuous action rather than a sequence of individual photos, we can be fooled into thinking that life is ongoing action when it is, in fact, a sequence of individual micro-happenings. Living in the moment is training ourselves to pay more attention to those individual frames and not letting them simply flow by unattended, not letting them become an indistinct part of life's ongoing drama. Rest comes from slowing down to the speed of now.

The Scriptures encourage us to make today our primary focus and not to dwell overly much on yesterday or tomorrow:

"This is the day the LORD has made;
We will rejoice and be glad in it."

PSALM 118:24, NKJV

"Therefore do not worry about tomorrow,
for tomorrow will worry about itself."

MATT. 6:34, NIV

Calmness and rest come when we allow ourselves to focus on what is and not on what was or what might be. It shrinks life down to a much more manageable size. We don't have to juggle as many balls at one time. We avoid the de-energizing effect of distracted thinking. Our focus is not even on today, but on each immediate portion of today.

Society is all about hurry, rush, multi-tasking, deadlines, and running to avoid being overtaken, all of which are poison to present moment living. In order to discover new dimensions of rest, we need to create for ourselves a new normal. It is decidedly counter-culture and only we can make it happen.

Many of us have spent so much time mentally living outside the present that we have a hard time imagining what it might be like and how it can be done. What should be normal has become unusual and exceptional.

I walk/jog in the morning. It begins with stretching, then a brisk walk for about thirty yards to warm up. When I come to the tan, walled-in townhouses, I break into a jog until I get past the last unit. Another brisk walk is followed by a jog from the fire station to the far end of police headquarters. Brisk walk again. At the fourth palm tree, I jog to the intersection. That walk/jog pattern repeats itself past three ball parks, a motel, condos, apartment houses, and back into our neighborhood.

I remember my first attempts to "live in the moment" during that exercise routine. My self-talk went something like this:

OK, take an inventory of my thoughts. What's going on up there?

To-do list. Nope, that's the future.

Getting hungry. What to have for breakfast? Nope, the future again.

Enjoyed seeing our daughter last night. Nope, the past.

Idea for the chapter I am writing. The future.

Need a new pair of sneakers. The future.

Chocolate cake. Definitely the future.

Hope that new noise in the car isn't a big, money sucking problem. The past and future.

This isn't working. Not as easy as I thought.

Focus. How about what's going on around me?

So many cars turning into office buildings. Man they get up early. Wonder what they're thinking about?

Duck under overhanging branch.

There's someone walking their dog. Must be a pain to have to pick up after them and then carry that little plastic bag of "doggie business" back home. Takes commitment. Note to self – never get a dog.

Hadn't noticed how the ground crew cares for the kids' ball field, smoothing out the dirt, trimming grass. What a blessing to have a great place to play, night lights included.

What do I need to prepare for that meeting at 4 p.m.? Nope. Future again.

Senses. Yea, that's it. Check in with my senses.

Feel – *Wind in my face. Coolish. Tingly on my cheeks. Refreshing. Heart rate coming up. Left foot a little sore. Starting to sweat. Deep breaths feel great. In through the nose, flaring slightly. Out through the mouth. Chest expanding.*

See – *That group of palm trees has an unusual leaf pattern. So long and elegant. Look at the huge pine cones under that tree. So perfectly shaped. Why hadn't I noticed them before? Wow, look how the pink, pre-sunrise glow is illuminating those pure white clouds! What do you call those kinds of clouds anyway? Cumulous? Cirrus? Never can remember.*

Hear – *Birds. Must be over a hundred in that flock up there squawking away. Where are they going? They always seem so skittish. Darting around? Any actual leader? Is this migration season? Can't be. Warbling in a tree nearby. Another type of bird. What an incredible song. How do they make those exotic sounds? Need to listen more carefully to pick up the pattern. Can I repeat some of it?*

Smell – *Not sure what I smell. Try again, more slowly. Ah, a hint of pine. Again. Is that Lavender? Roses? Definitely some musk in there. And fresh cut grass. Love it.*

And so it goes. It takes practice, but there is definitely a sense of freedom and lightness that comes over me when I get into the moment. The more I practice, the easier it becomes. The more I do it, the more I'm able to tune into what each moment has to offer. I am helped by remembering the brief but compelling Jewish prayer:

> *"Days pass, years vanish, and we walk sightless among miracles."*[79]
>
> **LYNNE M. BAAB**

As author Cari Murphy writes, "Allow the beauty of *now* to flood your consciousness and enjoy every little gift that comes your way."[80]

When I think of living in the present I get a strong mental image of childhood. The apostle Paul warned about being child*ish* and irresponsible (see 1 Cor. 13:11). But Jesus himself urged us to become more child*like* by viewing life from a humble, receptive, open point of view (see Matt. 18:2-4).

Children who grew up in the days before kindergarten and kindergarten prep school seemed to be freer to roam and explore back then like a lamb in the back forty. Absent video games, they woke up each day with a sense of adventure and created their own fun. The immediacy of life back then was one of the major keys to having a restful mind.

You may say, "But I'm not a kid anymore. I have responsibilities and obligations. Life is not as simple as it used to be." Of course adults have more to be concerned about than children, but that shouldn't rob us of the opportunity to retain or regain much of our former childhood attitudes and perspectives. When we grow up, we tend to leave behind too many of our childhood skills as if they are no longer needed or allowed. Play and wonder are two of the biggies. Living in the moment is another.

Giving ourselves the gift of the present doesn't mean we don't give thought to the future through planning and preparation. It doesn't mean we don't reflect on the past to draw lessons and reflect. It does mean that we are in the present a majority of the time.

The goal is not to be always upbeat and joyful, because not every experience in life is pleasant. The goal, instead, is to be *fully alive,* to have all of our senses awake, and to open our minds and hearts to what is happening in each part of the day. It's not just about slowing down, but engaging life and *living at a savoring pace.*[81] Relish what you are currently doing. You can't rush and relish at the same time. Everything changes, even how the sun illuminates an object. Almost everything is different every time you experience it.

Feelings can be a good indicator of whether or not your mind has strayed from the present. If you feel annoyed, frustrated, anxious, sad, guilty, or uptight, examine your thoughts to see if your mind has wandered away from *now*. You have most likely been either anticipating or replaying rather than anchoring in the present.[82]

We need to make a proactive choice to focus mainly on those feelings that are linked to current circumstances. That choice can affect something as simple as eating a chocolate chip cookie. The temptation is to compare it to other cookies from the past and say, "This isn't nearly as good as the one I had last week," which makes us disappointed rather than luxuriating in the current cookie for its own sweet, delicious sake.[83]

> *"Normal day, let me be aware of the treasure you are. Let me learn from you, love you, bless you before you depart."*
>
> **MARY JEAN IRON**

The following are some further keys to living in the moment:

1. **Acceptance opens many doors to the present.** It removes the natural resistance to engaging some events. Jay Dixit explains this perspective as, "…being open to the way things are in each moment without trying to manipulate or change the experience – without judging it, clinging to it, or pushing it away. The present moment can only be as it is. Trying to change it only frustrates and exhausts you. Acceptance relieves you of this needless extra suffering."[84]

2. **Gratefulness also directs our attention to the present.** We appreciate the varied experiences of life for what they can teach us and how they can help us grow.

3. **There are many activities that we do almost mindlessly.** Slowing down and noticing can open up new possibilities. Chores at home, for instance, can cause our thoughts to stray from the moment. Instead, use the following method to become more engaged:[85]

    a. Notice what chores you find boring.

    b. Pick one and choose to be fully present when you do it, utilizing all of your senses.

    c. Consider how what you are doing benefits others. Link the chore to making them healthy and happy. Personalize the activity and value the opportunity to serve your loved ones in this way. Connect it to the warm feelings you have for them.

4. **Routines at work can also cause our minds to wander.** Consider these possibilities:[86]

    a. Don't compare it to other tasks that seem more energizing. Avoid thinking, "I can't wait to get this done so that..."

    b. Change how you do the task. For instance, try using your non-dominant hand for part of the time. Alter the sequence or method.

    c. View the details with the eye of an artist. Notice details as if you had to paint the scene later.

    d. Think of how what you are doing serves the company, even in a small, unnoticed way.

    e. Set new goals such as becoming more efficient.

    f. Make a game of it. See how you might make some or all of it fun.

5. **Recognize that living in the moment makes us more productive.** Joseph Bailey writes,

    "I began to make the quality of each moment more important than getting things done, yet to my surprise, I actually was able to get more done with less effort and more enjoyment."[87]

6. **Focusing on your breathing** is a powerful way to propel yourself into the present. Usually we take breathing for granted, since it happens automatically. But when you focus your attention on that life-sustaining process for even a minute or two, you are present in the present.

We'll close this lesson with a memorable quote by Mary Jean Iron:

"Normal day, let me be aware of the treasure you are. Let me learn from you, love you, bless you before you depart. Let me not pass you by in quest of some rare and perfect tomorrow. Let me hold you while I may, for it may not always be so. One day I shall dig my nails into the earth, or bury my face in the pillow, or stretch myself taut, or raise my hands to the sky and want, more than all the world, your return."[88]

DISCUSSION

Describe what living in the present was like for you as a child. How much of that is still part of your life today?

....

....

Where do you spend most of your time mentally during non-work hours – in the past, present, or future?

....

....

What comes to mind when you think of living life at a "savoring pace"?

....

....

When your thoughts are drawn to events that happened earlier, what kinds of things do you tend to think about the most? What is the effect on you?

....

....

What is it about the future that most often captures your thinking? What is the impact on you?

....

....

What would it mean for you to be fully present at home?

....

....

How could you use your five senses to experience the present more fully tomorrow?

....

....

How can you become more satisfied by no longer comparing this moment to others?

....

....

....

SHARING

OPPORTUNITY #4:

- Pray for God to open the way for you to share something from these lessons to help someone else this week.
- Keep your radar up each day for opportunities.

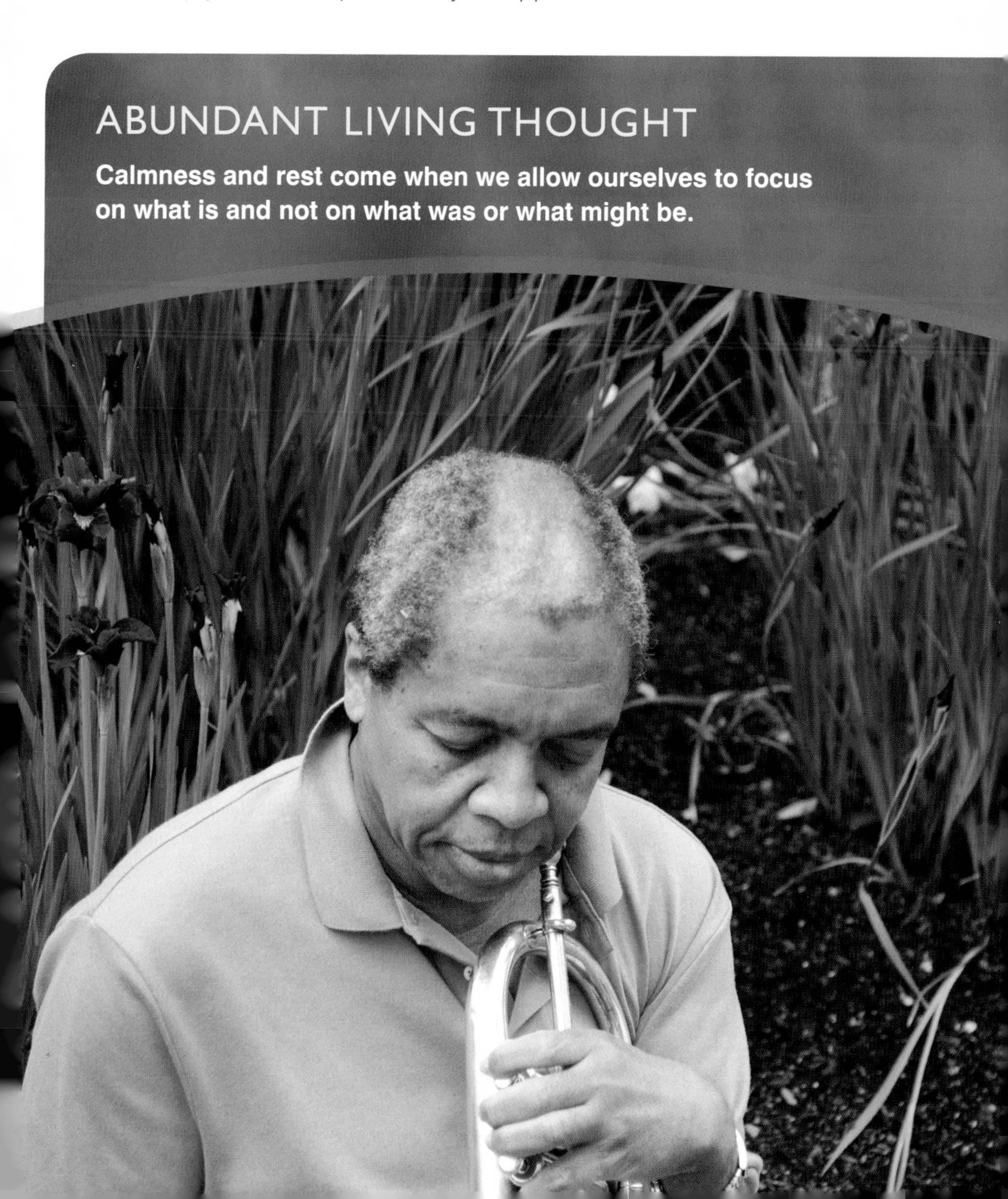

ABUNDANT LIVING THOUGHT

Calmness and rest come when we allow ourselves to focus on what is and not on what was or what might be.

GOOD THINKING
LESSON FIVE

WARM UP

Feedback: In what ways did God open the door last week for you share some part of the lessons with someone else?

Choose one or both questions to discuss (if in group setting) or write out your answers on a separate sheet (for individual use):

1. **What do people compliment you on the most?**[89]

2. **What is one of your most important goals at this point in your life?**[90]

"Multitasking means you are living several experiences at the same time, under the illusion that more is better as you exchange peace for pace."

DES CUMMINGS JR., PHD

DISCOVERY

Last year I stepped into the pantry at our house and spotted a small collection of light brown, dust-like particles on the tile floor. Immediately my mind screamed, "Sawdust!" "Termites!"

All sorts of anxiety-producing thoughts quickly bombarded my thinking: *Was the house in danger of collapse because the termites had munched through too many timbers? How many walls would have to be opened to find out? Would they have to put one of those big tent things over our house in order to fumigate? How would we pay for the huge repair bill? Would the house lose tons of value?* My heart raced and I shuddered at the awful possibilities.

An exterminator eventually arrived, examined the little particles closely for what seemed like an eternity, and finally declared nonchalantly, "This doesn't involve termites at all."

He then looked up at the wire shelving above and eyed a plastic bag of beans. "You better throw this out," he advised. "It's got bugs." The harmless insects had been eating the beans. Their dinner leftovers had spilled onto the floor through bug created holes.

The over-the-top fear that followed my pantry discovery was completely self-induced. It all stemmed from runaway thoughts. They created potential scenarios, that led to feelings, which stimulated even more anxious thoughts. Around and around, a world of trouble swirling inside my worry-prone head.

The good news is that circumstances like that don't have to dictate how we respond. They don't have to control our thoughts and feelings. We can either react in a knee jerk fashion or we can take charge of our own thought process. During the bean bug episode, I simply reacted and let my anxieties and insecurities take over by default. But there is a much better, more rest-inducing way. It begins with recognizing the role we play in our own restfulness of mind. It begins with taking back control.

This lesson is intended to address those normal, everyday situations when our minds get unnecessarily worked up and over-stressed... those times when we make mental mountains out of relative molehills... those times when we overreact and ruin our rest. It is not intended to focus on the extremes of psychological disorders or how to deal mentally with truly serious life events. The focus here is on the middle, what the majority of people experience during the give and take of regular living.

It is often the case that our own thoughts, rather than the circumstances themselves, create our inner reality. Thoughts are powerful and can cause feelings of unrest in ways unrelated to the actual situation.[91] The unrest can be a slight twinge or full-blown anxiety, but it frequently begins with our own thinking.[92]

For instance, many people rejoice when the circus comes to town. But others are annoyed because of the increased traffic. The circus itself is relatively neutral. It doesn't necessarily *cause* one reaction or the other, the people create the reactions within themselves.[93]

Or suppose your boss doesn't smile at you as you pass each other in the hallway. Your thought machine floods your mind with negative thinking: *I must have said something that upset him. I must have messed up on that last report. He's out to get me.*

The choice is ours to pay attention to these random thoughts or not. Better to choose more innocent interpretations unless you see unambiguous, objective evidence to the contrary: *He must be in a big rush and have lots of important issues on his mind. He must not be feeling well.*

Which thoughts we pay attention to is largely a matter of perspective and how we frame the issue internally.

Whenever we feel stress or unrest, it is important to realize that our thinking can be aggravated by misuse of what I'll call the "Problem Solving Brain." That amazing part of our mind can analyze and figure out mathematical equations, balance budgets, fix machines, create gadgets, choose which outfit to wear, do crossword puzzles, and on and on.[94]

People frequently misuse the Problem Solving Brain, however, by analyzing what should not be analyzed. A negative thought pops into our head and we not only give it our attention, we put it on a pedestal and examine it from every conceivable angle until we feel miserable and overwhelmed.

Society teaches us to be in problem solving mode most of the time. Instead of being a skill that is used only when needed, that part of our brain has become our dominant way of processing. Rest comes from putting that analytic portion of our mind in a lock box and pulling it out only when absolutely necessary to solve real problems, not imagined ones.[95]

Jesus warned us against overuse of our Problem Solving Brain by pointing to the worry-free life of birds:

"Look at the birds of the air; they do not sow or reap or store away in barns, and yet your heavenly Father feeds them. Are you not much more valuable than they? Can any one of you by worrying add a single hour to your life?"

MATT. 6:26, NIV

Imagine fifty sparrows sitting on a telephone wire strung about thirty feet up between two large poles in the state of Maine. Sparrow 34 in line is talking to 33 and 35 in late October:

34 – "I've been thinking."

33 – "Yah, what's up?"

34 – "Shouldn't we have started migrating already?"

33 – "Well, the leaves have definitely dropped off the trees."

34 – "If we stay here much longer we could get snowed in you know. Frozen ground. No food."

35 – "Scary thought alright."

34 – "My stomach's been feeling pretty queasy lately. Probably an ulcer from migration anxiety."

33 – "Or maybe you ate a bad worm or somethin'. You been snacking on road kill?"

34 – "That last flight around the pasture left me a little winded. Hope I can keep up when we finally get going. If I get left behind its curtains."

35 – "I was wheezing some myself."

34 – "And look at my tail feather sticking out back there. It's gonna create a ton of drag."

33 – "Yah, and smog is another problem. Too many cities on the way south. Any of you guys ever heard about beak rot?"

34 – "And the hawks. Those killing machines could take any of us down."

That doesn't happen. Sparrows don't over-think or over-analyze. They don't manufacture trouble and stress. Our own serenity will come from following their example.

We can help ourselves to remain inwardly restful by learning to distinguish between helpful and harmful thinking. A short list of harmful thoughts could include: exaggeration, catastrophizing (focusing only on the worst imaginable explanation), generalization (one problem means *everything* is a problem), self-deprecation, forecasting (if today is bad, tomorrow will be worse), and distortion. My anxiety over the pantry incident could have been largely avoided if I realized that I had fallen into the trap of exaggeration and catastrophizing.

In order to avoid getting drawn into harmful mental pathways, we need to learn to *not take all thoughts equally seriously.* Human beings tend to treat all thoughts as significant for two reasons:

a. We can watch a scary movie and know it isn't real because it is outside of ourselves. Our inner thoughts are very different, however. They are part of us, they exist within our heads, which makes them harder to ignore. The truth is that our thoughts don't necessarily equal reality at all, any more than the movie. As one author puts it, "Thinking is an ability, rather than a reality."[96] Thoughts can be only thoughts.[97]

b. We figure that if our brain took the time to generate the thought, it must have done so for an important reason. But we all know that our brains can produce thoughts that are serious or nonsense, useful or useless, sane or crazy, rational or absurd. Rather than saying to yourself, "If I think it, it must have some validity," tell yourself, "There's another thought, it may deserve my attention or it may not."[98] The fact is that our brains are thought producing machines.

The following list contains several additional keys to maintaining a peaceful, restful mind:

1. Teach your mind to stay on a life-giving path by regularly practicing a positive mental habit in a variety of situations, starting with the least difficult and expanding from there. We can develop pathways of peace for our brain to revert to when challenges to rest come our way.

2. Learn from the times when you did succumb and allowed circumstances to dictate your response. Ask yourself, "Why did that happen? What could I have done differently? What can I learn for the future?"

3. If possible, reduce exposure to the circumstance that triggered your negative thinking until your mind can get back onto a more restful track. For example, even though the bean bug particles didn't actually cause my anxiety, I could have helped myself by not examining them on the floor fifty times before the exterminator arrived.

4. Invite God to actively help shift your thinking toward inner rest. In the Old Testament book of Isaiah, we read this promise:

> ***"You will keep him in perfect peace, Whose mind is stayed on You, Because he trusts in You"***
>
> **ISA. 26:3, NKJV**

Memorizing Scripture and storing up God's promises give us the wherewithal to overcome debilitating thinking. The apostle Paul also offers the following advice,

"The weapons we fight with are not the weapons of the world. On the contrary, they have divine power to demolish strongholds. We demolish arguments and every pretension that sets itself up against the knowledge of God, and we take captive every thought to make it obedient to Christ" (2 Cor. 10:4-6, NIV).

Paul calls on us to subject every thought to the filter of whether or not it reflects Christ's principles and his desires for us.

5. Get rid of negative thoughts by *crowding them out.* Mentally shift focus. Starve bad thoughts by turning your attention to more healthful ones. This replacement technique becomes easier if you proactively make positive "thought deposits" ahead of time by engaging in activities such as Bible study and prayer. Negative thoughts eventually fade if we don't dwell on them or give them credence.

6. Potentially check in with a family member and/or trusted friend regarding persistent, anxiety-producing thoughts. Ask, "Am thinking straight here?" In isolation, distorted thinking can become even more distorted and keep us at arm's length from peace.

7. Recognize that some situations are so impactful that they overwhelm our ability to sort out our thought processes at the time. Such intense circumstances hook into our feelings at a deep level and short-circuit our ability to stand back and choose a different mental pathway until sometime later. In their book, *The Resilience Factor,* authors Karen Reivigh, PhD and Andrew Shatte, PhD, comment, "In some cases, events are so severe that your reactions *are* driven by the event itself, not your beliefs about the event. When a loved one dies, the emotions that follow largely stem from the tragedy itself, not from one's interpretations of the tragedy."[99]

   The authors go on to say that our resilience in intense emotional situations – how quickly we can gain perspective and shift onto a healing mental course – will largely be determined by how often we have made such choices in the past. The more frequently we have selected inner rest in a variety of circumstances, the more quickly our minds will be able to recover and get back onto the path of peace.[100]

8. Be aware that some poisonous circumstances can exhaust our ability to sustain a life-giving thought pattern, and we may need, therefore, to carefully consider making a change. A horrendous boss or an abusive spouse can bombard our brains with such intense negativity that our own thought processes get distorted and we start to believe their terrible untruths. In such intense cases, we need to take appropriate action to restore our mental well-being, which may include seeing a mental health counselor.

We hear much about the need for bodily rest, but not nearly enough about inner rest for the mind. The quality of life we desire, and that God desires for us, will be determined mostly by "what is happening between our ears." Paying attention to this inner world and learning how to bring it under control is one of the most impactful things we can do to discover new depths of calmness and peace.

DISCUSSION

Have you ever gotten very anxious because you exaggerated a situation? Share what happened. How did you recover?

Why is it so easy to believe that outward circumstances always *cause* our reactions?

A husband comes home from work and says angrily, "My boss made me so upset today!" What might his wife say to help him find peace of mind?

What kinds of thoughts do you tend to take too seriously and over-analyze?

How can you decide whether a thought deserves your attention or not?

What are some realistic ways to think about a problem that do not cause stress?

What thoughts would be the most effective for you to use in crowding out negative, stressful thinking?

Describe a particularly memorable time when you experienced deep peace of mind. What was it like?

SHARING

OPPORTUNITY #5:

- Pray for God to open the way for you to share something from these lessons to help someone else this week.
- Keep your radar up each day for opportunities.

ABUNDANT LIVING THOUGHT

Rest comes from putting that analytic portion of our mind in a lock box and pulling it out only when absolutely necessary to solve real problems, not imagined ones.

SIMPLICITY

LESSON SIX

WARM UP

Feedback: In what ways did God open the door last week for you share some part of the lesson with someone else?

Choose one or both questions to discuss (if in group setting) or write out your answers on a separate sheet (for individual use):

1. **What kinds of things do you hate spending money on?**[101]

2. **Are there any things that you were once afraid of that you no longer fear?**[102]

"Our lives were meant for calm, not chaos."

THOMAS KINKADE

DISCOVERY

When faced with large, threatening storms, one of the first things ancient mariners did was to throw unnecessary cargo overboard to make the ship lighter. The Scriptures mention this tactic in the book of Jonah: "All the sailors were afraid and each cried out to his own god. *And they threw the cargo into the sea to lighten the ship"* (Jonah 1:5, NIV, emphasis added).

The intrepid apostle Paul also talks about sailors employing a similar strategy when the ship he was traveling on got caught up in a fierce gale: "We took such a violent battering from the storm that the next day *they began to throw the cargo overboard"* (Acts 27:18, NIV, emphasis added).

I get a mental picture of boxes bobbing in the sea and large, sealed urns momentarily rolling with the waves then slipping under the whitecaps. The seamen had their priorities straight – *life is more important than stuff.*

My wife, Ann, periodically urges me to "lighten our ship." I have too many half-read books, shirts that are too small, pants that are too filthy, tools that are never used, memorabilia that has been boxed away for years, papers and seminar folders that are outdated, unused ointments and creams, etc. I used to be able to trick her when she was away by taking a few of my useless things from one part of the house and hiding them in another. Later, I'd point to their former location and say, "There, doesn't that look a whole lot better?" Now she's onto me and usually asks, "Ok, where'd you conceal it all this time?"

Eventually much of my useless stuff winds up in the garage. The garage is like one of those swirling whirlpools out in the ocean where junk gets ensnared forever. The final step from the garage to the Salvation Army pickup or the dump has so far proven to be a little too daunting. I sense, however, that the days of my garage treasures are numbered.

The truth is that Ann is right; pretty much all of it needs to go. My patient wife has a much better understanding of one of the keys to restful living than I do – *simplicity*. That concept has become a mantra in our family that she is teaching me to appreciate more and more.

Over time, we have come to understand that simplicity is about much more than getting rid of stuff. At its root, simplicity is about *freedom*.[103] As the old Quaker hymn tells us, "'Tis the gift to be simple, *'Tis the gift to be free"* [104] (emphasis added)

Simplicity is about freedom from:

- materialism
- commercialism
- workaholism
- the rat race.

Simplicity is about freedom to:

- live holistically
- live out the values modeled in the life of Christ
- find true rest.

Simplicity begins as an inward attitude that extends outward. It is as much about our minds as it is about our actions. It becomes a central value that governs our choices. It sets us on a course that is in many ways counter-cultural. The apostle Paul put his finger on a key element of simplicity when he encouraged us to throw off *everything* that hinders, including cultural norms (see Heb. 12:1-2).

The daily lives of most Americans are jammed with busyness. We are overcommitted and over-scheduled. We lack time to rest, unwind, reflect, and renew. We lack space for ourselves.

If books were printed like our lives are lived there wouldn't be any margins at all. It would be all text out to the edges.[105] Actually, to mimic the way we live, the text in a book would be *wider* than the edges of the paper. Text wouldn't fit 100 percent of the page, it would cover 120 percent. We might call them *negative margins*. A bunch of text would just be missing, having dropped off the sides.

Author Richard Swenson writes, "Now that we have exceeded so many of our limits – personal, emotional, relational, physical, financial – we have no margin at all. Yet because we don't even know what margin is, we don't realize it is gone. We know that something is not right, but we can't solve the puzzle beyond that. Our pain is palpable, but our assailant remains unnamed."[106]

To truly simplify our lives, we need to make room for margins. Trying to "find room" doesn't work. We have to create it by decreasing or removing other commitments and activities. Creating room for us to thrive, inwardly and outwardly, means re-thinking the American lifestyle and our own measures of success.

The following is a summary list of some of the counter-culture keys to simplicity that many have found helpful:

1. **Do nothing.** Society says that our worth is determined by our productivity, how much we get done. Christianity says our worth is determined very differently. It is a gift from a loving God who values us regardless of how much we make or earn. One of the best ways to say a resounding "no" to society's perspective is to do absolutely nothing. Start by doing nothing at home. Feet up, head back, arms relaxed by your side. Just put your body and thoughts in neutral.

   Extend out from there to doing nothing while you wait in line at the market. No worrying about the cost of what's in your basket. No reading magazines. No trying to remember what you forgot. Next, do nothing while you drive except drive. No radio, CDs, texting, calling, applying make-up, or multi-tasking. Simply doing nothing is like poking a finger in the eye of our production crazed world. Schedule periods of "nothing" in your week and stick to it.

   Legendary baseball pitcher, Satchel Page, observed, "Sometimes you need to sit and think. Sometimes you need to just sit."[107]

2. **Cut back on TV watching.** I have come to realize that I am addicted to watching the morning and evening news. Simplicity and freedom dictate breaking away from all addictions. What do I think I'm going to miss if I don't watch? News reporters typically scan several counties each day to tell us all about the stupidest, meanest, laziest, weirdest people they can find. Once that list is exhausted, they move on to fires and natural disasters. You'd think the world outside my door is a zoo where all the animals are on the loose. Do I feel more rested after the thirty minute broadcast is over? I don't think so!

3. **Spend less than you earn and control credit cards.** Financial simplicity is about prioritizing and spending according to our values. Years ago, my wife and I ran up a shocking $7,000 balance on our credit cards. After working very hard to pay off that huge amount, we determined that we would only use a credit card for trips and to not allow balances to carry over from one month to the next. The mental freedom and rest we have experienced since those dreadful days of debt is priceless. If you can't control credit cards, cut them up.

4. **Reject materialism.** We are bombarded with sales pitches to purchase items we don't really need. TV commercials make you feel like a Neanderthal if you don't have the latest whatever. And how could you even think about going outside in an outfit that makes the wrong fashion statement. Scandalous! I especially love the drug company actors. They spend the first 50 seconds telling you all about the wonders that await you by simply downing certain pills. Then, in the last 10 seconds, they have someone inform you in a soothing, pleasant voice that if you actually take the pills your brain could fall out, you could become mentally unstable, and your innards will gradually rot.

   The less we expose ourselves to commercial propaganda the better. Simplicity tells us to enjoy what Graham Hill calls "The luxury of less." [108] Jesus told us clearly, "Be on your guard against all kinds of greed; life does not consist in an abundance of possessions" (Luke 12:15, NIV). Richard Foster counsels, "The inward reality of simplicity involves a life of joyful unconcern for possessions." [109]

5. **Take a regular vacation from technology.** Smart phones and other wonders of technology have revolutionized communication in amazing ways. We have access to the world at our finger tips. I'm not very fast at texting, but I appreciate it.

   As valuable as these tools are, I am very concerned about excess. Too many kids become mesmerized by the virtual world on their smart phones or computers.

   Life is becoming techno-centered rather than people- and real-life centered. Too many individuals substitute virtual relationships for face-to-face conversations. So monitor how technology might be compromising your quest for simplicity. Observe its influence and be willing to take vacations from gadgets in order to keep perspective and balance. Give the electronics a rest periodically in order to optimize your rest of mind and soul.

6. **Slow down.** Take a deep breath and schedule less in your day. Walk and talk slower. Eat a lot slower. Every time we gulp our food in order to get to the next appointment or activity, we reinforce our adherence to the hectic, mindless rat race that surrounds us. Eating slowly, taking small bites, chewing deliberately, and savoring the smells and tastes builds a bulwark, brick by gastro-intestinal brick, against society's crazy pace. It is huge vote for sanity and relishing life's pleasures.

> *"Sometimes you need to sit and think. Sometimes you need to just sit."*
>
> **SATCHEL PAGE**

7. **Set boundaries.** Make a list of what's most important to you and then set firm boundaries to protect what's on it. It is our duty to say "no" when our limits are being encroached upon. My list of priorities would include:

    a. Relationship with God and spiritual growth.

    b. Emotional energy. When our emotional reserves are depleted or overdrawn, everything else in life is compromised. We should never have to apologize for choices that keep us emotionally healthy.

    c. Mental breaks and stimulation.

    d. Physical rest and exercise.

    e. Family time.

    f. Work.

    g. Fun and play.

8. **Consider downsizing.** Rather than working your head off to maintain your current lifestyle, consider taking your activities and possessions down a notch or two. Smaller house? Smaller car? Smaller TV? Smaller wardrobe? Fewer trips to the golf course? Fewer times eating out? Simpler vacations?

9. **Take delight in simple things.** Resist the need to experience large, loud, manufactured events in order to be fulfilled. Rediscover the marvels of nature or the pleasure of family games.

10. **Always ask,** "Will this simplify my life or complicate it further?"

John Kabit-Zinn, Professor of Medicine at the University of Massachusetts Medical School, sums up well the spirit of simple living, "Voluntary simplicity means going fewer places in one day rather than more, seeing less so I can see more, doing less so I can do more, acquiring less so I can have more." [110]

The apostle Paul also gives us some excellent counsel on having an inner attitude of simplicity when he writes, "I've learned by now to be quite content whatever my circumstances. I'm just as happy with little as with much, with much as with little" (Phil. 4:11-12, The Message).

NOTES:

Simplicity begins as an inward attitude that extends outward. It is as much about our minds as it is about our actions. It becomes a central value that governs our choices.

DISCUSSION

Give your own definition of the word "simplicity."

If you were to toss out one thing in your life, what would it be, physically or mentally?

Are there adequate margins in your life? If not, what could help expand them?

What would you do if you had more time for yourself?

Do you feel guilty about doing nothing? Why or why not?

What would a day be like for you without technology? Would it decrease your stress or increase it? Why?

Do you have a hard time saying "no" in order to preserve your own boundaries? If so, why is that the case?

If you had applied the test "Will this simplify my life?" what decisions from the past twelve months would you have made differently?

SHARING

OPPORTUNITY #6:

- Pray for God to open the way for you to share something from these lessons to help someone else this week.
- Keep your radar up each day for opportunities.

ABUNDANT LIVING THOUGHT

Simplicity begins as an inward attitude that extends outward. It is as much about our minds as it is about our actions.

BREATHING EASY

LESSON SEVEN

WARM UP

Feedback: In what ways did God open the door last week for you share some part of the lessons with someone else?

Choose one or both questions to discuss (if in group setting) or write out your answers on a separate sheet (for individual use):

1. **What do you feel that you take for granted the most in life right now?[111] Explain.**

2. **What would you do with your "15 minutes of fame?"[112]**

"Proper breathing can help you relax."

MONICA REED, MD

DISCOVERY

I have this thing about the little mail boxes at the post office. In the town where I grew up, each one was like a miniature safe with a dial surrounded by the numbers 1-10 and its own super-secret combination. If you dialed the right numbers, presto, the door opened and out came the surprise. Of course you expect the utility bill as well as junk mail from a local politician, but, and here's where the mystique comes in, there just might be a letter from a long lost semi-rich Aunt Josephine in Des Moines with a check in it for $10,000! She saw a photo of you in an old album and felt impressed to share. That's probably enough money to buy every toy in the department store!

One memorable day, my dad actually became the postmaster in the office just across the railroad tracks behind our house. He was the guy who reset the combinations when someone died or moved away. As a boy, I sneakily watched him do it several times, utterly fascinated.

As an adult, I was assigned to retrieve the mail each morning from the company's gigantic mail box downtown. Tons of mail, but what it gained in capacity it lacked in wonderment. After all, it was very unlikely that Aunt Josephine would use the company address.

The human body, of course, is not like a post office, even though some people may treat it as if it were. The heart, lungs, kidneys, brain, stomach, liver, and other organs do not operate independently like little mail boxes, with no interaction or integration with other parts. No element of our being can work at its best individually without considering how it is affected by other aspects of the overall system.

The parts of our body are more like a mobile, those whirly-gig things you hang over a baby's crib. Each part is separate, hanging from one of many wires. But here's the thing; if you touch one part, everything else is affected. One part moves, they all move. The entire mobile is completely interactive. That's what makes it unique.

Like touching a mobile, stress impacts not just one area of our body but many at the same time. It cannot affect our neck or shoulders without also rippling throughout other elements of our biology. Therefore, if we are to find true rest, the antidote to stress, we have to consider methods that have a broad influence. They must be designed to give systemic relief.

This lesson is devoted to introducing you to three solutions that have that kind of pervasive impact – *Deep Breathing, Progressive Relaxation,* and *Contemplation.* These rest-inducers are offered in the hope that you will not simply read about them, but actually choose to make them an integral part of your lifelong journey toward optimal health.

DEEP BREATHING

Each of your lungs is like an upside down tree with lots of branches called *bronchi* and tiny leaves called *alveoli.* When you suck in air, the alveoli expand like tiny balloons. Each balloon is surrounded by very small blood vessels, called capillaries, which draw in oxygen and dump off carbon-dioxide. Every red blood cell travels through the lungs on every trip around the body, making this life-giving oxygen/carbon dioxide exchange.[113]

Breathing is powered in part by a muscle – the diaphragm – that separates the chest from the abdominal cavity. When you inhale, the diaphragm is flexing downward pushing your abdomen out and expanding the chest. When the diaphragm relaxes it moves upward expelling the carbon dioxide, opening room for the next inhalation.[114]

Stress tenses up the diaphragm and interferes with its natural movement and limiting its range. To compensate, we "chest breathe," using our chest and shoulder muscles to expand the rib cage and draw in air. This produces a much shallower, inefficient breath that actually increases tension.[115]

The antidote is a period of deep breathing, which re-establishes a healthy pattern. You can do deep breathing while lying down, sitting, or standing. If you are sitting or standing, keep your back straight and head erect. Here's what one session of deep breathing would involve:

1. **Become aware of your breathing,** something we normally take for granted.
2. **Breathe slowly and deeply** in and out through your nostrils rather than your mouth. This serves to cleanse the air somewhat and adds warmth and moisture.[116]
3. **Notice what is happening with your chest and stomach.** On each inhalation your stomach should rise first and then your chest. For the exhalation, the chest should come down first and the stomach last. This gets your diaphragm fully involved. It may take some practice. You can rest one hand on your stomach and the other on your chest to make the movement more conspicuous.

4. **Count each inhalation and exhalation up to ten.** For example, inhale (one), exhale (two), inhale (three), exhale (four), etc. If you lose count, start again at one. It may be helpful to maintain the count for the full breath such as "o-o-o-n-n-e" for the inhalation and "t-w-o-o-o" for the exhalation.[117]

5. **Repeat several times a day, especially when stressed.** It will be a gift to every part of your mind and body.

We usually focus primarily on the inhalation as we take in oxygen from the atmosphere. To increase your awareness of your breathing, focus instead on the *exhalation.* Plants thrive on carbon dioxide, so picture yourself as doing your part to help the grass and trees in your backyard grow! At times make the exhalation even longer than the inhalation to force out more carbon dioxide and make room for an even larger draft of oxygen.[118]

"And He said to them, 'Come aside by yourselves to a deserted place and rest a while.' For there were many coming and going, and they did not even have time to eat."

MARK 6:31, NKJV

PROGRESSIVE RELAXATION

Stress typically causes a tensing of the muscles. You can release that tension by progressively tightening your muscles beyond normal and then relaxing them, one muscle group at a time. The following exercise should be done five to ten minutes each day at least, especially when subjected to stress:[119]

1. **Sit or lie down comfortably** with your arms at your sides.
2. **Do at least one cycle** of deep breathing.
3. **Tighten your fists and arms.** *Hold for seven seconds and release.* Let your arms dangle. Shake them out.
4. **After ten seconds, move on to the next body part.** Sequentially tighten and relax the following, one at a time: forehead, eyes, jaw and neck, shoulders and chest, stomach, your sit muscles, right leg and foot (extend outward), left leg, and foot. Hold each for seven seconds, release, then wait ten seconds.
5. **Is there any tension left?** If so, repeat for that body part. You can use this technique any time of the day. As you become more adept, you can vary the exercise by doing it a bit more quickly such as holding for five seconds and releasing for five.

CONTEMPLATION

Contemplation is defined by *The American Heritage Dictionary* as, "To ponder or consider thoughtfully."[120] One of the most helpful ways to do that is to make time on a regular basis for a period of quiet reflection.

Focused contemplation requires commitment, but it is relatively easy to do. It can take as little as five to ten minutes a day, but can, of course, be longer. It is usually done while sitting comfortably, with good posture, on a chair or cushion away from distractions as much as possible. Early morning is often the best time. The following is a typical contemplation process, but there are variations:

1. **Calm yourself.** Progressive relaxation works very well in this regard.
2. **Be fully present in the moment.** Tune your awareness in to what is happening now. The goal here is to draw the mind away from distracting thoughts about the past or the future, be they positive or negative. A helpful way to do that is to pay careful attention to your breathing. Take one or two minutes to do some deep breathing here. It relaxes you, focuses your attention, and prepares your mind for calm reflection.
3. **Choose the content of your contemplation.** Many people find the Bible to be a particularly fruitful source for focusing their thoughts. Its grand themes and practical wisdom are ideal for capturing our attention and renewing our spirit. The Scriptures themselves provide guidance regarding some of the spiritual themes you might choose, underlined in the following examples:

   "Within your temple, O God, we meditate on your unfailing love" (Ps. 48:9, NIV).

   "I meditate on your precepts and consider your ways" (Ps. 119:15, NIV).

   "Cause me to understand the way of your precepts, that I may meditate on your wonderful deeds" (Ps. 119:27, NIV).

   "My eyes stay open through the watches of the night, that I may meditate on your promises" (Ps. 119:148, NIV).

If the Scripture verse you chose is rather long, take a small portion of it for contemplation such as, *My peace I give to you (John 14:27); Blessed are the poor in spirit (Matt. 5:3); Don't be afraid (John 6:20); You are worth more than many sparrows (Luke 12:7), etc.* You can also summarize the verse into a brief phrase and personalize it such as, *Jesus is my friend (see Luke 5:20).*

You are not studying so much as simply reflecting. The goal is not scholarly analysis but absorption. Mentally repeat the verse or your paraphrase and let its meaning soak into your thoughts. Listen for any impressions or applications that the Holy Spirit may present.

You can also try to imagine a scene from Scripture. Make it come alive. Imagine that you are an on-site observer. Call upon your senses to recreate the event. What is there to see, hear, feel, smell, and taste? You can also become one of the characters in the scene and see it through their eyes.

4. **Bring your thoughts back into focus.**

The Lord counsels us in Scripture, "Be still, and know that I am God" (Psalm 46:10, NKJV). The biggest challenge is the "be still" part. Our minds are usually so preoccupied with the busyness of the day that it can be hard for them to calm down and zero in on a particular subject. That requires patience and gentle retraining.

You can count on your mind meandering all over the place, especially at first. It is important not to react to these distractions or to judge them in any way.[121] Let them simply float in and out of your mind like the clouds passing overhead. Gently but firmly bring your thoughts back to the content you have chosen.

Our minds are trained by life to be scattered multitaskers, so be patient with yourself. Some days it will be harder to rein your thoughts in than others. Gradually it should get easier as your mind catches on. If a particular thought won't go away, take a moment, write it down, and then focus back on your breathing first and then your content.

> It is the distracting thoughts that bombard us throughout the day that cause so many of our negative feelings. Putting these life-sapping thoughts aside through contemplation, even for just five to ten minutes a day, allows our minds to rest and heal, and that healing will eventually spill over to affect our entire outlook and overall well-being.

Jesus set an example for us when he called a time out in his ministry so he and his disciples could recoup mentally and physically.

> *"And He said to them, 'Come aside by yourselves to a deserted place and rest a while.' For there were many coming and going, and they did not even have time to eat. So they departed to a deserted place in the boat by themselves" (Mark 6:31-21, NKJV).*

We are holistic beings and it is essential that we also regularly call a time out in our busy lives to deepen our shallow breathing, relax our tense muscles, and lift our harried minds above the stresses of the day by contemplating spiritual themes.

Rest, in all its various forms, is an essential element of abundant living. It balances the hectic pace of modern life and provides the mental, physical, and spiritual renewal we need in order to thrive.

DISCUSSION

If studying in a group, have the entire group go through one session of deep breathing as outlined in the lesson.

Have you ever been in a stressful situation where taking deep breaths helped you cope? Describe.

If studying in a group, have the entire group go through one session of progressive relaxation as outlined in the lesson for the following body parts: *fists, arms, forehead, eyes, jaw, neck and shoulders* (skip the deep breathing step which you have already done).

Describe a situation when you plan to use deep breathing and/or progressive relaxation this coming week.

If studying in a group, have the entire group spend time in contemplation (skip the progressive relaxation and deep breathing steps which you have already done). Choose a short verse of Scripture that everyone will reflect on for three minutes. Afterward, share impressions that came to people's minds. How hard was it to focus?

In what ways do you take short time-outs during the week? Describe.

What is the most effective way for you to keep your mind focused when extraneous thoughts intrude?

SHARING

OPPORTUNITY #7:

- Pray for God to open the way for you to share something from these lessons to help someone else this week.
- Keep your radar up each day for opportunities.

ABUNDANT LIVING THOUGHT

It is essential that we regularly call a time out in our busy lives to deepen our shallow breathing, relax our tense muscles, and lift our harried minds above the stresses of the day.

THE BEST REST

LESSON EIGHT

WARM UP

Feedback: In what ways did God open the door last week for you share some part of the lessons with someone else?

Choose one or both questions to discuss (if in group setting) or write out your answers on a separate sheet (for individual use):

1. **Have you ever won anything? Describe.**

2. **If you gave a talk to a third grade class, what would the subject be?**

*"Come to me,
all of you who are
weary and carry
heavy burdens, and
I will give you rest."*

JESUS CHRIST

DISCOVERY

I'd never imagined going hiking at night. My wife and I saw the ad, looked at each other with a "Hey, why not" smirk, and signed up. About seven couples met at a park, gathered for instructions from our leader, and set off with considerable trepidation about thirty minutes after sunset.

To my surprise, once our eyes adjusted, the small slice of moon provided enough light to see adequately. What is an ambling, nonchalant walk during the daytime took on a heightened sense of delightful mystery throughout the evening. I could make out shapes, contours, all made eerily distinctive by the absence of color. Tense with anticipation, people hardly spoke.

We snaked among the trees and bushes, taking note of details and contrasts that would have been far less conspicuous at other times. Oddly configured branches were mistaken for silhouettes of animals or birds. My thoughts lifted easily to the God who created everything around us.

At one point, the leader signaled everyone to gather around at the base of a slight incline. In hushed tones, she told us about the owls that inhabited the area. Owls, of course, love the night. Our location, a couple of miles from civilization, put us squarely in their territory. The leader took a small tape recorder from around her neck and told us she planned to play owl calls to see if we could get a response.

Everyone leaned in. The silence grew palpable as every ear strained. We heard the slight click of the "play" button. Then several short hoots from the tape. Silence. More recorded hoots. Silence. The anticipation made it slightly harder to breathe. Then it happened. No mistaking it. From deep in the woods to our left, "Hoooo, Hoooo, HooHoooo."

The recorder played an answering call. Again the swivel headed, large eyed owl somewhere high up in the branches replied. Then another off to our right. And another, even closer. The world stood still. All else faded. Magical is the only word that came to mind.

On that night of undisturbed quietness and thoroughly engaging intentionality, my wife and I entered a world far different from the rush of a normal day. It had coaxed all of our senses to a new level, expanded our awareness, and deepened our gladness. We had accessed an experience that made the other days richer.

The Bible talks about a God-given invitation to enter into a similar experience once each week. It is not so much about owls and night hikes, but about mirroring the dynamics of that memorable outing and more. It is about the same kind of heightened awareness, focused intentionality, and magical quietness. *It is called the Sabbath day.*

The Sabbath is an opportunity to enter a world where God, family, and friends are given the undivided attention they deserve. It is a time to focus on things that matter most and engage in nourishing self-care. It beckons us to step aside for twenty-four hours from the damaging influences of relentless work pressures, pervasive materialism, the unending rat race, and corrosive anxiety.

I have been keeping the Sabbath for over forty years and cannot imagine life without it. It is a tremendous source of rest and renewal. Jesus was an avid Sabbath keeper (see Luke 4:16). He even referred to himself as "Lord of the Sabbath" (Mk. 2:28). The disciples integrated it fully into their lives as well.

The origins of the Sabbath take us back to the Bible account of Creation in the book of Genesis. During five extraordinary days, God made everything in the natural world, from roses to chimpanzees. On the sixth day he made Adam and Eve, the first human beings. He then surveyed his extraordinary accomplishments and labeled everything very good. The Scriptures then tell us what happened at the end of that eventful week: "By the seventh day God had finished the work he had been doing; so on the seventh day he rested from all his work. Then God blessed the seventh day and made it holy, because on it he rested from all the work of creating that he had done" (Gen. 2:3, NIV).

What was originally made for an ideal world before sin has become an even more vital lifeline since sin began. All the compelling characteristics of Sabbath have flowed from Eden down through the centuries to benefit us today. Having been created for humanity's first parents, it is intended for all their descendants from all corners of the earth. If we are at all interested in optimal living, Sabbath has to be a central consideration.

The description of the day in Genesis emphasizes three main points:

1. **God *rested.***
2. **He *blessed* the day.**
3. **He made it *holy*.**

Those same three elements are mentioned again centuries later when God gave the Ten Commandments from Mount Sinai. It makes particular reference back to the events of Creation: "Remember the Sabbath day by keeping it holy. Six days you shall labor and do all your work, but the seventh day is a Sabbath to the LORD your God. On it you shall not do any work... For in six days the LORD made the heavens and the earth, the sea, and all that is in them, but he *rested* on the seventh day. Therefore the LORD *blessed* the Sabbath day and *made it holy.* (Exodus 20:8-11, NIV).

Let's look at these three key elements more closely in relation to Sabbath keeping.

RESTED

God rested on the final day of creation week not because he was weary, but as a sign that he was finished and also as an example for us. The original word for "rested" in Genesis 2 is *shabath,* which literally means to cease from labor.[122] That original day of rest established the model and pattern for all Sabbath keeping since. The biblical day went from sundown to sundown, marking out the time for us to put aside our regular work and focus on God's agenda for that special twenty-four hour period.[123]

Imagine a thirty-five year old administrative assistant named Sue who works for a large, multi-national corporation headquartered in New York City. She is employed by one of the small branch stores in rural North Dakota. Sue has been there for ten years. Wednesday morning she gets a remarkable phone call from the CEO of the entire worldwide operation, Sarah Stiles. Sue has seen her large, formal portrait in the hallway downstairs. Pleasant. Well dressed.

"Hello, is this Susan?" Sarah, the CEO, begins.

Sue offers a nervous, "Yes, this is she."

"Sue, I'm getting reports that you seem exhausted most of the time. Taking work home nights and weekends. Plus you're a single mom with two small children. You are a very valuable person, so I want you to take a full day away from all work every weekend. You are too important to let you burn out. I can help figure out the scheduling and work load. If anyone gives you a hassle about it, refer them to me. OK?"

"Uh, I guess so. Thanks so much."

Wouldn't it be great to get a phone call like that? That's exactly what happens with the Sabbath, except the phone call comes from God, the CEO of the entire universe! He understands that we need a weekly Sabbath break from work in order to function as he intended. He wants to provide a special environment within which we can rest, grow, and heal.

God asks us to refrain from work in order to get our attention. He knows it takes time and quietness to listen to him. It also takes time to listen to others. It takes time to listen well to our own inner selves.

Sabbath protects us from the dehumanizing effects of our fast paced society. It shouts that we are human *beings,* not human *doings.*[124] We get to put away the to-do-lists and abstain from anything that smacks of productivity or achievement. We even get to sleep in and take a long nap.

Sabbath reminds us that God doesn't love us because of what we do, but simply because of who he is. It is his very nature to love and it cannot be earned. On that special day, mankind's doing is taken out of the equation and replaced with his marvelous grace.[125]

It is our relationship with Christ that is at the center of true Sabbath keeping. In the gospel of Matthew, he links that relationship with deep, ongoing rest: "Come to Me, all you who labor and are heavy laden, and I will give you rest. Take My yoke upon you and learn from Me, for I am gentle and lowly in heart, and you will find rest for your souls. For My yoke is easy and My burden is light" (Matt. 11:28-30, NKJV).

Christ talks about "rest for your souls," rest for your inner self, that sensitive place where anxiety and stress normally hang out and bully you around. There are only two requirements to obtain this precious gift: (1) take his yoke, which means letting him direct your life, and (2) learn from him and his ways.

Sabbath also restores the proper work/rest balance.[126] Without that corrective, we can become like machines, functionaries, and forget our status as children of a wonderful heavenly Father. The work/rest balance that Sabbath fosters needs to be kept in mind during the other days of the week as well. It does no good to be a workaholic for six days and then come to the Sabbath exhausted. That completely misses the larger life lesson.[127]

A twenty-four hour period given to holistic rest will be viewed by many in our production-obsessed world as excessive and wasteful. But God knows what we need far better than the misguided gurus of modern culture. For those who say they are too busy to adopt such a lengthy period away from work at the office or at home, I point to the testimony of countless Sabbath keepers who have discovered that they are *more* productive during the other six days because they feel so refreshed and renewed.[128]

BLESSED

The Sabbath is a veritable cornucopia of blessings. It is a time to get in touch with our spirit and emotions that have been masked all week by our hectic schedules. We can pay attention to what our heart is telling us, as well as our head. It can put us back in touch with our hopes and dreams, re-centering our values and life purpose.[129] As Abraham Heschel has written, "The Sabbath is a day for the sake of life."[130]

The Old Testament prophet Isaiah tells us that the Sabbath is a time for celebration:

> *"If you watch your step on the Sabbath*
> *and don't use my holy day for personal advantage,*
> If you treat the Sabbath as a day of joy,
> God's holy day as a celebration,
> *If you honor it by refusing 'business as usual,'*
> *making money, running here and there –*
> *Then you'll be free to enjoy God!*
> *Oh, I'll make you ride high and soar above it all"*
> *(Isa. 58:13-14, The Message).*

We celebrate the Sabbath day by praising God, remembering his promises, worshipping together, drawing closer to family, nurturing friendships, taking time to nourish our body, mind, and spirit, offering gratitude, and serving those in need. Also, time spent in nature on Sabbath is a great way to calm our jittery nerves, uplift our souls, and gain precious insights into the heart of the Master Designer.

MADE IT HOLY

In order to be in tune with the holiness that God built into the Sabbath, we need to take special time on that day to focus on our relationship with him. Sabbath is a weekly opportunity to renew our understanding of his place in our lives.

At times, we can forget who is ultimately in charge. God is the Creator and we are the created. Remembering that fact allows us to avoid living as if everything depended on us.[131] As creatures, we are limited in our capacity and understanding. We are easily distracted and can neglect essential spiritual things. Sabbath calls us to remember how much bigger God is than all of our problems, how he knows the end from the beginning, and never grows weary. We are reminded that he has more than enough resources to see us through.

Ultimate rest from fear and worry comes from the assurance that we are in God's care and can relinquish our destiny to his all-wise control.

Jesus once remarked that "the Sabbath was made for man, and not man for the Sabbath" (Mark 2:27, KJV). It is God's amazing elixir to restore and renew his children. It is his bulwark against all that would compromise his beneficent intentions. It is truly *the best rest.*

10 IDEAS TO ENHANCE SABBATH REST

1. **LEARN FROM GOD'S WORD**
   - Bible studies for adults. Bible story books and games for children.
   - Role-play Bible stories.
   - Pretend to interview Bible characters. Record and then play back.
2. **DRAW CLOSER AS A COUPLE/FAMILY**
   - Celebrate each person's unique talents and personality.
   - Dialogue about each person's hopes/dreams/needs/experiences.
   - Take time to listen well.
3. **EXPERIENCE HOLISTIC REST**
   - Sleep in and/or take a nap. Take a hot, aromatic bath.
   - Read a great book that uplifts your soul and renews your spirit.
   - Take a rest from technology – no phone, computer, tablet, or TV.
4. **WORSHIP**
   - Have family worship time in the home by reading, singing, praying.
   - Participate in corporate worship at church.
   - Take time for personal prayer and meditation.
5. **DEVELOP TRADITIONS**
   - Bring flowers into the house to begin each Sabbath.
   - Wear clothes reserved for Sabbath.
   - Light Sabbath candles.
6. **EAT SPECIAL MEALS**
   - Eat a lunch that the whole family helps prepare.
   - Have the same kind of Sabbath breakfast each week.
   - Invite people to share a meal together at home or have a picnic.
7. **EXPLORE NATURE**
   - Plan a picnic in the park and hike to your desired spot.
   - Visit the zoo and admire God's incredible creations.
   - Go canoeing and take pictures of the wildlife you see.
8. **SERVE PEOPLE IN NEED**
   - Do random acts of kindness.
   - Help at a soup kitchen.
   - Send encouragement cards or deliver fruit baskets.
9. **BE CREATIVE**
   - Play music or do an art project.
   - Arrange flowers.
   - Write in a gratitude journal. Compose a poem.
10. **STRENGTHEN SOCIAL TIES WITH OTHERS**
    - Attend a small group.
    - Volunteer to read to patients at the hospital.
    - Write a letter to a loved one you haven't spoken with in a while.

DISCUSSION

Share a time when you experienced nature in a surprising or novel way.

Is Sabbath new to you or have you experienced it already?

How do you think society has suffered from not emphasizing Sabbath?

What ideas do you have regarding what to do on Sabbath?

Which of the benefits from Sabbath keeping do you need the most right now?

If studying in a group, share one of your most memorable moments.

Are there any ways that you feel a greater sense of rest than you did eight weeks ago?

Name one or two big "take-aways" from this study.

SHARING

OPPORTUNITY #8:

- Pray for God to open the way for you to share something from these lessons to help someone else this week.
- Keep your radar up each day for opportunities.

ABUNDANT LIVING THOUGHT

The Sabbath is an opportunity to enter a world where God, family, and friends are given the undivided attention they deserve.

NOTES:

ABOUT THE AUTHOR

Kim Johnson is a popular writer, speaker, and fervent advocate for holistic living. As the author of three books, eleven lesson series, and many articles, his writings focus on healthy living and spiritual connectedness. His materials have been used in hundreds of churches throughout North America and internationally as well.

Johnson is an ordained minister with more than 35 years of experience as a parish pastor and church administrator. Over the years, his work with parishioners emphasized principles of whole-person health as a path to optimum mental, physical, social, and spiritual well-being. His later work with pastors and church leaders emphasized skill development such as vision casting, goal setting, support systems, relationship management, and accountability. Johnson has put his experience of working with pastors and parishioners to use in the CREATION Health Life Guide Series by creating a resource ideally suited for use in churches, small groups, or individual study.

Johnson holds a Master of Divinity degree and received his Bachelor of Arts in theology. He currently serves as Director of Resource Development for churches in the state of Florida. His personal interests include reading, classical music, art and book festivals, kayaking, traveling, volunteering, and small group study. He and his wife Ann make their home in Orlando.

Author Acknowledgements: It has been a great privilege for me to be associated with the team of dedicated individuals who helped in various ways to make these CREATION Health Life Guides available. I would like to single out my wife Ann and daughter Stefanie, whose feedback and suggestions were always characterized by unfailing support and clear-eyed honesty. I have also received invaluable guidance and encouragement from Mike Cauley, Tim Nichols, Nick Howard, and Jim Epperson. Finally, I want to thank the group of local pastors who met with me personally and provided a wonderful forum for evaluating the lesson drafts.

NOTES

1. Garry Poole, *The Complete Book of Questions* (Grand Rapids, MI: Zondervan, 2003), 59.
2. Garry Poole, *The Complete Book of Questions*, 73.
3. "Why You Shouldn't Skimp on Sleep," October 20, 2008, http://www.sleepfoundation.org/alert/why-you-shouldnt-skimp-sleep.
4. Dr. James B. Maas, *Power Sleep* (New York, NY: Quill, 2001), 51.
5. Lawrence Epstein, MD, *The Harvard Medical School Guide to A Good Night's Sleep* (New York, NY: McGraw-Hill, 2007), 15.
6. Sara C. Mednick, PhD, *Take A Nap! Change Your Life* (New York, NY: Workman Publishing, 2006), 33.
7. Dr. James B. Maas, Power Sleep, 26.
8. Sara C. Mednick, PhD, *Take A Nap! Change Your Life,* 33.
9. Sara C. Mednick, PhD, *Take A Nap! Change Your Life,* 35.
10. Sara C. Mednick, PhD, *Take A Nap! Change Your Life,* 35.
11. Sara C. Mednick, PhD, *Take A Nap! Change Your Life,* 38.
12. Dr. James B. Maas, *Power Sleep,* 32.
13. Dr. James B. Maas, *Power Sleep,* 32.
14. Sara C. Mednick, PhD, *Take A Nap! Change Your Life,* 39.
15. Lawrence Epstein, MD, *The Harvard Medical School Guide to A Good Night's Sleep,* 15-16.
16. Sara C. Mednick, PhD, *Take A Nap! Change Your Life,* 39.
17. Sara C. Mednick, PhD, *Take A Nap! Change Your Life,* 40.
18. Lawrence Epstein, MD, *The Harvard Medical School Guide to A Good Night's Sleep,* 17; Sara C. Mednick, PhD, *Take A Nap! Change Your Life*, 41.
19. Lawrence Epstein, MD, *The Harvard Medical School Guide to A Good Night's Sleep,* 15; Sara C. Mednick, PhD, *Take A Nap! Change Your Life,* 41.
20. Dr. James B. Maas, *Power Sleep,* 37.
21. Dr. James B. Maas, *Power Sleep,* 38.
22. Dr. James B. Maas, *Power Sleep,* 39.
23. Sara C. Mednick, PhD, *Take A Nap! Change Your Life,* 44.
24. Dr. James B. Maas, *Power Sleep*, 34; Lawrence Epstein, MD, The Harvard *Medical School Guide to A Good Night's Sleep*, 5; Matthew Edlund, MD, *The Power of Rest* (New York, NY: HarperOne, 2010), 31-32; Sara C. Mednick, PhD, *Take A Nap! Change Your Life*, 17; "Obesity and Sleep," http://www.sleepfoundation.org/article/sleep-topics/obesity-and-sleep; "How Much Sleep Do We Really Need?" http://www.sleepfoundation.org/article/how-sleep-works/how-much-sleep-do-we-really-need.
25. Garry Poole, *The Complete Book of Questions*, 79.
26. Dr. James B. Maas, *Power Sleep*, 51-52.
27. Sara C. Mednick, PhD, *Take A Nap! Change Your Life*, 21.
28. Dr. James B. Maas, *Power Sleep*, 54; Lawrence Epstein, MD, *The Harvard Medical School Guide to A Good Night's Sleep*, 47.
29. Sara C. Mednick, PhD, *Take A Nap! Change Your Life,* 12.

30. Dr. James B. Maas, *Power Sleep,* 8.
31. Dr. James B. Maas, Power Sleep, 7.
32. Lawrence Epstein, MD, *The Harvard Medical School Guide to A Good Night's Sleep,* 6.
33. Sara C. Mednick, PhD, *Take A Nap! Change Your Life,* 12.
34. Lawrence Epstein, MD, *The Harvard Medical School Guide to A Good Night's Sleep,* 6.
35. U.S. Department of Health and Human Services, "Crash in Bed Not on the Road," http://www.nhlbi.nih.gov/health/public/sleep/healthy_sleep.pdf.
36. Dr. James B. Maas, *Power Sleep*, 73.
37. "Health Concerns: Insomnia," http://www.lef.org/protocols/lifestyle_longevity/insomnia_01.htm.
38. "Get Moving and Quit Tossing and Turning," http://www.my-coach.com/sleep/articles/get-moving-and-quit-tossing-and-turning.
39. "How to Sleep Better," http://helpguide.org/life/sleep_tips.htm.
40. Science News, "Early to Bed and Early to Rise: Study Suggests It's Keeping Kids Leaner," September. 30, 2011, http://www.sciencedaily.com/releases/2011/09/110930052216.htm; Frederick P., "When is the Best Time to Sleep?" http://www.ineedmotivation.com/blog/2007/10/when-is-the-best-time-to-sleep/; Annie B. Bond, "Sleep Secrets," May 3, 2003, http://www.care2.com/greenliving/sleep-secrets-how-to.html.
41. Dr. Michael Breus, "How to Find Your Bodies Best Bedtime," May 26, 2011, http://www.huffingtonpost.com/dr-michael-j-breus/best-bedtime_b_866290.html?ref=sleep.
42. Dr. James B. Maas, *Power Sleep,* 74.
43. Charlotte Libov, "Trouble Sleeping? Some Bedtime Snacks Can Help You Sleep," July 16, 2012, http://www.webmd.com/sleep-disorders/features/trouble-sleeping-some-bedtime-snacks-can-help-you-sleep.
44. "Eat Your Way to a Better Night's Sleep," http://www.my-coach.com/sleep/articles/eat-your-way-better-nights-sleep. "7 Tips for the Best Sleep Ever," http://www.health.com/health/gallery/0,,20407230_4,00.html.
45. Vivian Diller, PhD, "Sleep Like A Baby At Any Age," 10-4-2011, http://www.huffingtonpost.com/vivian-diller-phd/tips-for-better-sleep_b_988637.html.
46. Dr. James B. Maas, *Power Sleep,* 77.
47. "How to Sleep Better," http://www.wikihow.com/Sleep-Better.
48. William Wordsworth, "To Sleep," http://www.netpoets.com/classic/poems/073033.htm.
49. Garry Poole, *The Complete Book of Questions,* 117.
50. Barbara Ann Kipfer, *4,000 Questions for Getting to Know Anyone and Everyone* (New York, NY: Random Houose Reference, 2004), 9.
51. Sara C. Mednick, PhD, *Take A Nap! Change Your Life,* 4.
52. Sara C. Mednick, PhD, *Take A Nap! Change Your Life,* 5.
53. Sara C. Mednick, PhD, *Take A Nap! Change Your Life,* 7.
54. Dr. James B. Maas, *Power Sleep,* 132.
55. Matthew Edlund, MD, *The Power of Rest,* 93

56. Lawrence J. Epstein, MD, *The Harvard Medical School Guide to A Good Night's Sleep,* 20.
57. Dr. James B. Maas, *Power Sleep,* 125.
58. UC Berkeley News Center, Yasmin Anwar, "An afternoon nap markedly boosts the brain's learning capacity," Media Relations, February 22, 2010, http://newscenter.berkeley.edu/2010/02/22/naps_boost_learning_capacity/.
59. Harvey B. Simon, MD, "Caught Napping: Are afternoon naps OK?" Harvard Health Publications, http://health.msn.com/health-topics/sleep-disorders/caught-napping.
60. Margaret Minnicks, "Companies are encouraging 'nap time' on the job," August 22, 2011, http://www.examiner.com/workplace-issues-in-richmond/companies-are-encouraging-nap-time-on-the-job.
61. Angela Haupt, "Why Power Naps at Work Are Catching On," Nov 15, 2010, http://health.yahoo.net/articles/sleep/why-power-naps-work-are-catching.
62. Leslie Gebhart, "Have You Considered the Importance of Napping to Inspire Your Creativity the Artist's Way?" http://ezinearticles.com/?Have-You-Considered-the-Importance-of-Napping-to-Inspire-Your-Creativity-the-Artists-Way?&id=3513660.
63. Mayo Clinic Staff, "Napping: Do's and don'ts for healthy adults," http://www.mayoclinic.com/health/napping/MY01383/NSECTIONGROUP=2.
64. Elizabeth Scott, MS, "Sleep Benefits: Power Napping for Increased Productivity," *Stress Relief & Health,* July 07, 2008, http://stress.about.com/od/lowstresslifestyle/a/powernap.htm; Suzanne Arant-Wells, "The Benefits of Napping - For Adults," http://ezinearticles.com/?The-Benefits-of-Napping---For-Adults&id=800981.
65. National Sleep Foundation, "Napping," http://www.sleepfoundation.org/article/sleep-topics/napping.
66. Sara C. Mednick, PhD, *Take A Nap! Change Your Life,* 96; William A. Anthony, PhD, *The Art of Napping* (Burdett, NY: Larson Publications, 1997), 3; Camille W. Anthony, MEd, and William A. Anthony, PhD, *The Art of Napping at Work* (Burdett, NY: Larson Publications, 1999), 64.
67. Jonathan Abrams, "Napping on Game Day Is Prevalent Among NBA Players," *New York Times,* March 6, 2011, http://www.nytimes.com/2011/03/07/sports/basketball/07naps.html?pagewanted=2&_r=4.
68. Teresa M. McAlveavy, "Naps awaken productivity," 05/13/2007, http://www.denverpost.com/search/ci_5882726.
69. Angela Haupt, "Why Power Naps at Work Are Catching On," Nov 15, 2010, http://health.yahoo.net/articles/sleep/why-power-naps-work-are-catching.
70. Carlin Flora, "Nap Your Way to the Top," February 04, 2008, http://www.psychologytoday.com/articles/200802/nap-your-way-the-top.
71. Tony Schwartz, "Why Companies Should Insist That Employees Nap," *Harvard Business Review,* September 24, 2010, http://www.businessweek.com/managing/content/sep2010/ca20100924_895792.htm.
72. National Sleep Foundation, "Napping," http://www.sleepfoundation.org/article/sleep-topics/napping; Dr. Frank Lipman, "Snooze for Success: Power Naps Go Mainstream," April 29, 2011, http://www.huffingtonpost.com/dr-frank-lipman/power-naps-success_b_853243.html.
73. Sara C. Mednick, PhD, *Take A Nap! Change Your Life,* 51.
74. Matthew Edlund, MD, *The Power of Rest,* 92.

75. Tony Schwartz, "Why Companies Should Insist the Employees Nap," September 20, 2010, http://www.businessweek.com/managing/content/sep2010/ca20100924_895792.htm.
76. William A. Anthony, PhD, *The Art of Napping,* 4.
77. Barbara Ann Kipfer, *4,000 Questions for Getting to Know Anyone and Everyone,* 15.
78. Barbara Ann Kipfer, *4,000 Questions for Getting to Know Anyone and Everyone,* 32.
79. Lynne M. Baab, *Sabbath Keeping* (Downers Grove, IL: IVP Books, 2005), 75.
80. Cari LaGrange Murphy, *Create Change Now* (Mustang, OK: Tate Publishing & Enterprises, 2009), 56.
81. Kirk Byron Jones, *Addicted to Hurry* (Valley Forge, PA: Judson Press, 2003), 67, 74.
82. Richard Carlson and Jospeh Bailey, *Slowing Down to the Speed of Life* (New York, NY: HarperCollins, 1997), 52-53.
83. Jay Dixit, "The Art of Now: Six Steps to Living in the Moment, November 01, 2008, http://www.psychologytoday.com/articles/200810/the-art-now-six-steps-living-in-the-moment.
84. Jay Dixit, "The Art of Now: Six Steps to Living in the Moment," November 01, 2008, http://www.psychologytoday.com/articles/200810/the-art-now-six-steps-living-in-the-moment.
85. Jude, "How to make routine chores more fun," February 5, 2011, http://www.leadersbynature.com/blog/routine-chores-fun/.
86. "8 Ways to Make Routine Tasks Interesting," http://www.thechangeblog.com/8-ways-to-make-routine-tasks-interesting/.
87. Richard Carlson and Joseph Bailey, *Slowing Down to the Speed of Life* (New York, NY: HarperOne, 1997), 4.
88. "Quotations about Living in the Present," http://www.quotegarden.com/live-now.html.
89. Barbara Ann Kipfer, *4,000 Questions for Getting to Know Anyone and Everyone,* 49.
90. Jerry D. Jones, *201 Great Questions,* 21.
91. Richard Carlson, *You Can Be Happy No Matter What,* (Novator, California: New World Library, 2006), 12-15.
92. Richard A. Swenson, MD, *Margin* (Colorado Springs, CO: NavPress, 2004), 44.
93. Richard Carlson, *You Can Be Happy No Matter What,* 17, 21.
94. Richard Carlson and Joseph Bailey, *Slowing Down to the Speed of Life,* 26-27, 42.
95. Richard Carlson and Joseph Bailey, *Slowing Down to the Speed of Life,* 42.
96. Richard Carlson, *You Can Be Happy No Matter What,* 15.
97. Richard Carlson and Joseph Bailey, *Slowing Down to the Speed of Life,* 102.
98. Richard Carlson and Joseph Bailey, *Slowing Down to the Speed of Life,* 57.
99. Karen Reivich, PhD and Andrew Shatte, PhD, *The Resilience Factor* (New York, NY: Broadway Books, 2002), 91.
100. Karen Reivich, PhD and Andrew Shatte, PhD, *The Resilience Factor,* 91.
101. Barbara Ann Kipfer, *4,000 Questions for Getting to Know Anyone and Everyone,* 107.
102. Barbara Ann Kipfer, 4*,000 Questions for Getting to Know Anyone and Everyone,* 156.
103. Richard J. Foster, *Celebration of Discipline* (New York, NY: HarperCollins Publishers, 1998), 79.
104. Richard J. Foster, *Celebration of Discipline*, 79.

105. Mike Ronsisvalle, PsyD, *Stress Relief for Life* (Lake Mary, FL: Siloam, 2011), 152.

106. Richard A. Swenson, MD, *Margin* (Colorado Springs, CO: NavPress, 2004), 42.

107. Kirk Byron Jones, *Addicted to Hurry*, 94.

108. Graham Hill, "Less Stuff, More Happiness," September 12, 2011, http://www.huffingtonpost.com/2011/12/09/life-editing_n_1138817.html?ref=uk&ir=UK.

109. Richard J. Foster, *Celebration of Discipline,* 87.

110. John Kabat-Zinn, "Simplicity Quotes," June 7, 2010, http://sourcesofinsight.com/simplicity-quotes/.

111. Garry Poole, *The Complete Book of Questions*, 37.

112. "100 Get to Know You Questions," http://icebreakergames.net/100-get-to-know-you-questions/.

113. Craig Freudenrich, PhD, "How Your Lungs Work," http://science.howstuffworks.com/environmental/life/human-biology/lung.htm; Matthew McKay, PhD and Patrick Fanning, *The Daily Relaxer* (Oakland, CA: New Harbinger Publications, 2006), 17.

114. Matthew McKay, PhD and Patrick Fanning, *The Daily Relaxer*, 16-17.

115. Matthew McKay, PhD and Patrick Fanning, *The Daily Relaxer,* 17.

116. Matthew McKay, PhD and Patrick Fanning, *The Daily Relaxer,* 17.

117. Stephan Bodian, *Meditation for Dummies* (Indianapolis, IN: Wiley Publishing, Inc., 2006), 100.

118. Veronique Vienne, *The Art of Doing Nothing* (New York, NY: Clarkson Potter/Publishers, 1998), 20.

119. James Claiborn, PhD and Cherry Pedrick, *The Habit Change Workbook* (Oakland, CA: New Harbinger Publications, Inc., 2001), 70-71.

120. The American Heritage Dictionary, Second College Edition, (Boston, MA: Houghton Mifflin Company, 1982), 316.

121. Herbert Benson, MD, *The Relaxation Response* (New York, NY: Harper, 2000), 86.

122. Marva J. Dawn, *Keeping the Sabbath Wholly* (Grand Rapids, MI: William B. Eerdmans Publishing Company, 1989), 3.

123. Lynne M. Baab, *Sabbath Keeping* (Downers Grove, IL: InterVarsity Press, 2005), 14.

124. Lynne M. Baab, *Sabbath Keeping,* 35.

125. Lynne M. Baab, *Sabbath Keeping,* 17, 95.

126. Marva J. Dawn, *Keeping the Sabbath Wholly,* 17.

127. Marva J. Dawn, *Keeping the Sabbath Wholly,* 55.

128. Lynne M. Baab, *Sabbath Keeping,* 90.

129. Lynne M. Baab, *Sabbath Keeping,* 19.

130. Abraham Joshua Heschel, *The Sabbath* (New York, NY: Farrar, Straus and Giroux, 1951), 14.

131. Marva J. Dawn, *Keeping the Sabbath Wholly,* 30-31.

RESOURCES

SEMINAR MATERIALS

Leader Guide

Everything a leader needs to conduct this seminar successfully, including key questions to facilitate group discussion and PowerPoint™ presentations for each of the eight principles.

Participant Guide

A study guide with essential information from each of the eight lessons along with outlines, self assessments, and questions for people to fill-in as they follow along.

Small Group Kit

It's easy to lead a small group using the CREATION Health videos, the Small Group Leaders Guide and the Small Group Discussion Guide.

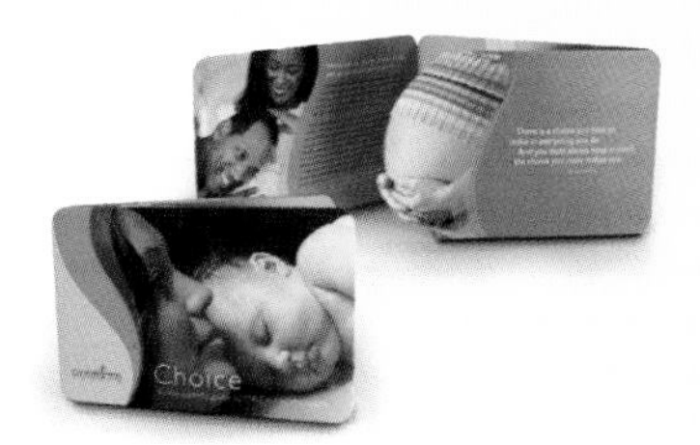

Senior Guide

Share the CREATION Health principles with seniors and help them be healthier and happier as they live life to the fullest.

Self-Assessment

This instrument raises awareness about how CREATION Healthy a person is in each of the eight major areas of wellness.

Pregnancy Guides

Expert advice on how to be CREATION Healthy while expecting.

GET ORGANIZED!

Tote Bag

A convenient way for bringing CREATION Health materials to and from class.

Smartphone App

The free CREATION Health App supplies daily health tips, weekly CREATION Conversation videos, and refreshing virtual vacations to break away from your day.

Presentation Folder

Keep CREATION Health notes and resources organized and in one place.

Pocket Guide

A tool for keeping people committed to living all of the CREATION Health principles daily.

MARKETING MATERIALS

Postcards, Posters, Stationary, and more

You can effectively advertise and generate community excitement about your CREATION Health seminar with a wide range of available marketing materials such as enticing postcards, flyers, posters, and more.

CREATION Health Discovery (Softcover)

CREATION Health Discovery takes the 8 essential principles of CREATION Health and melds them together to form the blueprint for the health we yearn for and the life we are intended to live.

CREATION Health Breakthrough (Hardcover)

Blending science and lifestyle recommendations, Monica Reed, MD, prescribes eight essentials that will help reverse harmful health habits and prevent disease. Discover how intentional choices, rest, environment, activity, trust, relationships, outlook, and nutrition can put a person on the road to wellness. Features a three-day total body rejuvenation therapy and four-phase life transformation plan.

CREATION Health Devotional (English: Hardcover / Spanish: Softcover)

Stories change lives. Stories can inspire health and healing. In this devotional you will discover stories about experiencing God's grace in the tough times, God's delight in triumphant times, and God's presence in peaceful times. Based on the eight timeless principles of wellness: Choice, Rest, Environment, Activity, Trust, Interpersonal relationships, Outlook, Nutrition.

CREATION Health Devotional for Women (English)

Written for women by women, the *CREATION Health Devotional for Women* is based on the principles of whole-person wellness represented in CREATION Health. Spirits will be lifted and lives rejuvenated by the message of each unique chapter. This book is ideal for women's prayer groups, to give as a gift, or just to buy for your own edification and encouragement.

8 Secrets of a Healthy 100 (Softcover)

Can you imagine living to a Healthy 100 years of age? Dr. Des Cummings Jr., explores the principles practiced by the All-stars of Longevity to live longer and more abundantly. Take a journey through the 8 Secrets and you will be inspired to imagine living to a Healthy 100

Forgive To Live (English: Hardcover / Spanish: Softcover)

In *Forgive to Live* Dr. Tibbits presents the scientifically proven steps for forgiveness – taken from the first clinical study of its kind conducted by Stanford University and Florida Hospital.

Forgive To Live Workbook (Softcover)

This interactive guide will show you how to forgive – insight by insight, step by step – in a workable plan that can effectively reduce your anger, improve your health, and put you in charge of your life again, no matter how deep your hurts.

Forgive To Live Devotional (Hardcover)

In his powerful new devotional Dr. Dick Tibbits reveals the secret to forgiveness. This compassionate devotional is a stirring look at the true meaning of forgiveness. Each of the 56 spiritual insights includes motivational Scripture, an inspirational prayer, and two thought-provoking questions. The insights are designed to encourage your journey as you begin to *Forgive to Live*.

Forgive To Live God's Way (Softcover)

Forgiveness is so important that our very lives depend on it. Churches teach us that we should forgive, but how do you actually learn to forgive? In this spiritual workbook noted author, psychologist, and ordained minister Dr. Dick Tibbits takes you step-by-step through an eight-week forgiveness format that is easy to understand and follow.

Forgive To Live Leader's Guide

Perfect for your community, church, small group or other settings.

The Forgive to Live Leader's Guide Includes:

- 8 Weeks of pre-designed PowerPoint™ presentations.
- Professionally designed customizable marketing materials and group handouts on CD-Rom.
- Training directly from author of Forgive to Live Dr. Dick Tibbits across 6 audio CDs.
- Media coverage DVD.
- CD-Rom containing all files in digital format for easy home or professional printing.
- A copy of the first study of its kind conducted by Stanford University and Florida Hospital showing a link between decreased blood pressure and forgiveness.

52 Ways to Feel Great Today (Softcover)

Wouldn't you love to feel great today? Changing your outlook and injecting energy into your day often begins with small steps. In *52 Ways to Feel Great Today*, you'll discover an abundance of simple, inexpensive, fun things you can do to make a big difference in how you feel today and every day. Tight on time? No problem. Each chapter is written as a short, easy-to-implement idea. Every idea is supported by at least one true story showing how helpful implementing the idea has proven to someone a lot like you. The stories are also included to encourage you to be as inventive, imaginative, playful, creative, or adventuresome as you can.

Pain Free For Life (Hardcover)

In *Pain Free For Life*, Scott C. Brady, MD, – founder of Florida Hospital's Brady Institute for Health – shares for the first time with the general public his dramatically successful solution for chronic back pain, Fibromyalgia, chronic headaches, Irritable bowel syndrome and other "impossible to cure" pains. Dr. Brady leads pain-racked readers to a pain-free life using powerful mind-body-spirit strategies used at the Brady Institute – where more than 80 percent of his chronic-pain patients have achieved 80-100 percent pain relief within weeks.

If Today Is All I Have (Softcover)

At its heart, Linda's captivating account chronicles the struggle to reconcile her three dreams of experiencing life as a "normal woman" with the tough realities of her medical condition. Her journey is punctuated with insights that are at times humorous, painful, provocative, and life-affirming.

SuperSized Kids (Hardcover)

In *SuperSized Kids*, Walt Larimore, MD, and Sherri Flynt, MPH, RD, LD, show how the mushrooming childhood obesity epidemic is destroying children's lives, draining family resources, and pushing America dangerously close to a total healthcare collapse – while also explaining, step by step, how parents can work to avert the coming crisis by taking control of the weight challenges facing every member of their family.

SuperFit Family Challenge – Leader's Guide

Perfect for your community, church, small group or other settings.

The SuperFit Family Challenge Leader's Guide Includes:

- 8 Weeks of pre-designed PowerPoint™ presentations.
- Professionally designed marketing materials and group handouts from direct mailers to reading guides.
- Training directly from Author Sherri Flynt, MPH, RD, LD, across 6 audio CDs.
- Media coverage and FAQ on DVD.